THE RED MAN'S CONTINENT

ABRAHAM LINCOLN EDITION

∴

VOLUME 1
THE CHRONICLES
OF AMERICA SERIES
ALLEN JOHNSON
EDITOR

GERHARD R. LOMER
CHARLES W. JEFFERYS
ASSISTANT EDITORS

Gravure Andréssen-Lamy, Lot N° 1

THE GREAT PALACE OF MITLA, OAXACA, MEXICO

Wood engraving in *Ancient Cities of the New World*, by Désiré Charnay, translated by J. Gonino and Helen S. Conant, published by Chapman and Hall, London, 1887.

THE
RED MAN'S CONTINENT

A CHRONICLE
OF ABORIGINAL AMERICA
BY ELLSWORTH HUNTINGTON

NEW HAVEN: YALE UNIVERSITY PRESS
TORONTO: GLASGOW, BROOK & CO.
LONDON: HUMPHREY MILFORD
OXFORD UNIVERSITY PRESS

1919

PREFACE

In writing this book the author has aimed first to present in readable form the main facts about the geographical environment of American history. Many important facts have been omitted or have been touched upon only lightly because they are generally familiar. On the other hand, special stress has been laid on certain broad phases of geography which are comparatively unfamiliar. One of these is the similarity of form between the Old World and the New, and between North and South America; another is the distribution of indigenous types of vegetation in North America; and a third is the relation of climate to health and energy. In addition to these subjects, the influence of geographical conditions upon the life of the primitive Indians has been emphasized. This factor is especially important because people without iron tools and beasts of burden, and without any cereal crops except corn, must respond to their environment very differently from civilized

vii

people of today. Limits of space and the desire to make this book readable have led to the omission of the detailed proof of some of the conclusions here set forth. The special student will recognize such cases and will not judge them until he has read the author's fuller statements elsewhere. The general reader, for whom this book is designed, will be thankful for the omission of such purely technical details.

CONTENTS

ILLUSTRATIONS

THE RED MAN'S CONTINENT

CHAPTER I

THE APPROACHES TO AMERICA

ACROSS the twilight lawn at Hampton Institute straggles a group of sturdy young men with copper-hued complexions. Their day has been devoted to farming, carpentry, blacksmithing, or some other trade. Their evening will be given to study. Those silent dignified Indians with straight black hair and broad, strong features are training their hands and minds in the hope that some day they may stand beside the white man as equals. Behind them, laughing gayly and chattering as if without a care in the world, comes a larger group of kinky-haired, thick-lipped youths with black skins and African features. They, too, have been working with the hands to train the mind. Those two diverse races, red and black, sit down together

1

in a classroom, and to them comes another race. The faces that were expressionless or merely mirthful a minute ago light up with serious interest as the teacher comes into the room. She stands there a slender, golden-haired, blue-eyed Anglo-Saxon girl just out of college — a mere child compared with the score of swarthy, stalwart men as old as herself who sit before her. Her mobile features seem to mirror a hundred thoughts while their impassive faces are moved by only one. Her quick speech almost trips in its eagerness not to waste the short, precious hour. Only a strong effort holds her back while she waits for the slow answers of the young men whom she drills over and over again in simple problems of arithmetic. The class and the teacher are an epitome of American history. They are more than that. They are an epitome of all history.

History in its broadest aspect is a record of man's migrations from one environment to another. America is the last great goal of these migrations. He who would understand its history must know its mountains and plains, its climate, its products, and its relation to the sea and to other parts of the world. He must know more than this, however, for he must appreciate how various environments alter man's energy and capacity and give his character a slant in one direction or another. He must also know the paths by which the inhabitants have reached their present homes, for the influence of former environments upon them may be more important than their immediate surroundings. In fact, the history of North America has been perhaps more profoundly influenced by man's inheritance from his past homes than by the physical features of his present home. It is indeed of vast importance that trade can move freely through such natural channels as New York Harbor, the Mohawk Valley, and the Great Lakes. It is equally important that the eastern highlands of the United States are full of the world's finest coal, while the central plains raise some of the world's most lavish crops. Yet it is probably even more important that because of his inheritance from a remote ancestral environment man is energetic, inventive, and long-lived in certain parts of the American continent, while elsewhere he has not the strength and mental vigor to maintain even the degree of civilization to which he seems to have risen.

Three streams of migration have mainly determined the history of America. One was an ancient and comparatively insignificant stream from Asia. It brought the Indian to the two great continents which the white man has now practically wrested from him. A second and later stream was the great tide which rolled in from Europe. It is as different from the other as West is from East. Thus far it has not wholly obliterated the native people, for between the southern border of the United States on the one hand, and the northern borders of Argentina, Chile, and Uruguay on the other, the vast proportion of the blood is still Indian. The European tide may in time dominate even this region, but for centuries to come the poor, disinherited Indians will continue to form the bulk of the population. The third stream flowed from Africa and was as different from either of the others as South is from North.

The differences between one and another of these three streams of population and the antagonisms which they have involved have greatly colored American history. The Indian, the European, and the Negro apparently differ not only in outward appearance but in the much more important matter of mentality. According to Brinton[1] the average brain capacity of Parisians, including

[1] D. G. Brinton, *The American Race.*

adults of both sexes, is 1448 cubic centimeters. That of the American Indian is 1376, and that of the Negro 1344 cubic centimeters. With this difference in size there appears to be a corresponding difference in function. Thus far not enough accurate tests have been made upon Indians to enable us to draw reliable conclusions. The Negro, however, has been tested on an extensive scale. The results seem to leave little doubt that there are real and measurable differences in the mental powers of races, just as we know to be the case among individuals. The matter is so important that we may well dwell on it a moment before turning to the cause of the differences in the three streams of American immigrants. If there is a measurable difference between the inherent brain power of the white race and the black, it is practically certain that there are also measurable differences between the white and the red.

Numerous tests indicate that in the lower mental powers there is no great difference between the black and the white. In physical reactions one is as quick as the other. In the capacity of the senses and in the power to perceive and to discriminate between different kinds of objects there is also practical equality. When it comes to the higher faculties, however, such as judgment, inventiveness, and the power of organization, a difference begins to be apparent. These, as Ferguson[1] says, are the traits that "divide mankind into the able and the mediocre, the brilliant and the dull, and they determine the progress of civilization more directly than do the simple fundamental powers which man has in common with the lower animals." On the basis of the most exhaustive study yet made, Ferguson believes that, apart from all differences due to home training and environment, the average intellectual power of the colored people of this country is only about three-fourths as great as that of white persons of the same amount of training. He believes it probable, indeed, that this estimate is too high rather than too low. As to the Indian, his past achievements and present condition indicate that intellectually he stands between the white man and the Negro in about the position that would be expected from the capacity of his brain. If this is so, the mental differences in the three streams of migration to America are fully as great as the outward and manifest physical differences and far more important.

Why does the American Indian differ from the

[1] G. O. Ferguson, *The Psychology of the Negro,* New York, 1916.

Negro, and the European from both? This is a question on which we can only speculate. But we shall find it profitable to study the paths by which these diverse races found their way to America from man's primeval home. According to the now almost universally accepted theory, all the races of mankind had a common origin. But where did man make the change from a four-handed, tree-dwelling little ape to a much larger, upright creature with two hands and two feet? It is a mistake to suppose that because he is hairless he must have originated in a warm climate. In fact quite the opposite seems to be the case, for apparently he lost his hair because he took to wearing the skins of slain beasts in order that he might have not only his own hair but that of other animals as a protection from the cold.

In our search for the starting-place of man's slow migration to America our first step should be to ascertain what responses to physical environment are common to all men. If we find that all men live and thrive best under certain climatic conditions, it is fair to assume that those conditions prevailed in man's original home, and this conclusion will enable us to cast out of the reckoning the regions where they do not prevail. A study of the relations of millions of deaths to weather conditions indicates that the white race is physically at its best when the average temperature for night and day ranges from about 50° to 73° F. and when the air is neither extremely moist nor extremely dry. In addition to these conditions there must be not only seasonal changes but frequent changes from day to day. Such changes are possible only where there is a distinct winter and where storms are of frequent occurrence. The best climate is, therefore, one where the temperature ranges from not much below the freezing-point at night in winter to about 80° F. by day in summer, and where the storms which bring daily changes are frequent at all seasons.

Surprising as it may seem, this study indicates that similar conditions are best for all sorts of races. Finns from the Arctic Circle and Italians of sunny Sicily have the best health and greatest energy under practically the same conditions; so too with Frenchmen, Japanese, and Americans. Most surprising of all, the African black man in the United States is likewise at his best in essentially the same kind of weather that is most favorable for his white fellow-citizens, and for Finns, Italians, and other races. For the red race, no

exact figures are available, but general observation
of the Indian's health and activity suggests that
in this respect he is at one with the rest of mankind.

For the source of any characteristic so widespread and uniform as this adaptation to environment we must go back to the very beginning of the
human race. Such a characteristic must have
become firmly fixed in the human constitution
before primitive man became divided into races,
or at least before any of the races had left their
original home and started on their long journey to
America. On the way to this continent one race
took on a dark reddish or brownish hue and its hair
grew straight and black; another became black-
skinned and crinkly-haired, while a third developed
a white skin and wavy blonde hair. Yet throughout the thousands of years which brought about
these changes, all the races apparently retained the
indelible constitutional impress of the climate of
their common birthplace. Man's physical adaptation to climate seems to be a deep-seated physiologi-
cal fact like the uniformity of the temperature of
the blood in all races. Just as a change in the
temperature of the blood brings distress to the individual, so a change of climate apparently brings
distress to a race. Again and again, to be sure, on

the way to America, and under many other circumstances, man has passed through the most adverse climates and has survived, but he has flourished and waxed strong only in certain zones.

Curiously enough man's body and his mind appear to differ in their climatic adaptations. Moreover, in this respect the black race, and perhaps the red, appears to be diverse from the white. In America an investigation of the marks of students at West Point and Annapolis indicates that the best mental work is done when the temperature averages not much above 40° F. for night and day together. Tests of school children in Denmark point to a similar conclusion. On the other hand, daily tests of twenty-two Negroes at Hampton Institute for sixteen months suggest that their mental ability may be greatest at a temperature only a little lower than that which is best for the most efficient physical activity. No tests of this sort have ever been made upon Indians, but such facts as the inventiveness of the Eskimo, the artistic development of the people of northern British Columbia and southern Alaska, and the relatively high civilization of the cold regions of the Peruvian plateau suggest that the Indian in this respect is more like the white race than the black. Perhaps man's mental powers underwent their chief evolution after the various races had left the aboriginal home in which the physical characteristics became fixed. Thus the races, though alike in their physical response to climate, may possibly be different in their mental response because they have approached America by different paths.

Before we can understand how man may have been modified on his way from his original home to America, we must inquire as to the geographical situation of that home. Judging by the climate which mankind now finds most favorable, the human race must have originated in the temperate regions of Europe, Asia, or North America. We are not entirely without evidence to guide to a choice of one of the three continents. There is a scarcity of indications of preglacial man in the New World and an abundance of such indications in the Old. To be sure, several skulls found in America have been supposed to belong to a time before the last glacial epoch. In every case, however, there has been something to throw doubt on the conclusion. For instance, some human bones found at Vero in Florida in 1915 seem to be very old. Certain circumstances, however, suggest that possibly they may not really belong to the layers

of gravel in which they were discovered but may
have been inserted at some later time. In the Old
World, on the contrary, no one doubts that many
human skulls and other parts of skeletons belong
to the interglacial epoch preceding the last glacial
epoch, while some appear to date from still more
remote periods. Therefore no matter at what date
man may have come to America, it seems clear
that he existed in the Old World much earlier.
This leaves us to choose between Europe and Asia.
The evidence points to central Asia as man's
original home, for the general movement of human
migrations has been outward from that region and
not inward. So, too, with the great families of
mammals, as we know from fossil remains. From
the earliest geological times the vast interior of
Asia has been the great mother of the world, the
source from which the most important families
of living things have come.

Suppose, then, that we place in central Asia the
primitive home of the thin-skinned, hairless human
race with its adaptation to a highly variable climate
with temperatures ranging from freezing to eighty
degrees. Man could not stay there forever. He
was bound to spread to new regions, partly because
of his innate migratory tendency and partly

because of Nature's stern urgency. Geologists are
rapidly becoming convinced that the mammals
spread from their central Asian point of origin
largely because of great variations in climate.[1]
Such variations have taken place on an enormous
scale during geological times. They seem, indeed,
to be one of the most important factors in evolution. Since early man lived through the successive
epochs of the glacial period, he must have been
subject to the urgency of vast climatic changes.
During the half million years more or less of his
existence, cold, stormy, glacial epochs lasting tens
of thousands of years have again and again been
succeeded by warm, dry, interglacial epochs of
equal duration.

During the glacial epochs the interior of Asia
was well watered and full of game which supplied
the primitive human hunters. With the advent
of each interglacial epoch the rains diminished,
grass and trees disappeared, and the desert spread
over enormous tracts. Both men and animals
must have been driven to sore straits for lack of
food. Migration to better regions was the only
recourse. Thus for hundreds of thousands of years
there appears to have been a constantly recurring

[1] W. D. Matthew, *Climate and Evolution*, N. Y. Acad. Sci., 1915.

outward push from the center of the world's greatest land mass. That push, with the consequent overcrowding of other regions, seems to have been one of the chief forces impelling people to migrate and cover the earth.

Among the primitive men who were pushed outward from the Asian deserts during a period of aridity, one group migrated northeastward toward the Kamchatkan corner of Asia. Whether they reached Bering Sea and the Kamchatkan shore before the next epoch of glaciation we do not know. Doubtless they moved slowly, perhaps averaging only a few score or a hundred miles per generation, for that is generally the way with migrations of primitive people advancing into unoccupied territory. Yet sometimes they may have moved with comparative rapidity. I have seen a tribe of herdsmen in central Asia abandon its ancestral home and start on a zigzag march of a thousand miles because of a great drought. The grass was so scanty that there was not enough to support the animals. The tribe left a trail of blood, for wherever it moved it infringed upon the rights of others and so with conflict was driven onward. In some such way the primitive wanderers were kept in movement until at last they reached the bleak

shores of the North Pacific. Even there something
— perhaps sheer curiosity — still urged them on.
The green island across the bay may have been so
enticing that at last a raft of logs was knotted together with stout withes. Perhaps at first the men
paddled themselves across alone, but the hunting
and fishing proved so good that at length they
took the women and children with them, and so
advanced another step along the route toward
America. At other times distress, strife, or the
search for game may have led the primitive nomads on and on along the coast until a day came
when the Asian home was left and the New World
was entered.

The route by which primitive man entered
America is important because it determined the
surroundings among which the first Americans
lived for many generations. It has sometimes been
thought that the red men came to America by way
of the Kurile Islands, Kamchatka, and the Aleutian Islands. If this was their route, they avoided
a migration of two or three thousand miles through
one of the coldest and most inhospitable of regions.
This, however, is far from probable. The distance
from Kamchatka to the first of the Aleutian Islands
is over one hundred miles. As the island is not in

sight from the mainland, there is little chance that
a band of savages, including women, would de-
liberately sail thither.   There is equally little probability that they walked to the island on the ice,
for the sea is never frozen across the whole width.
Nevertheless the climate may at that time have
been colder than now.   There is also a chance that
a party of savages may have been blown across to
the island in a storm.   Suppose that they succeeded
in reaching Bering Island, as the most Asiatic of
the Aleutians is called, the next step to Copper
Island would be easy.   Then, however, there comes
a stretch of more than two hundred miles.   The
chances that a family would ever cross this waste
of ocean are much smaller than in the first case.
Still another possibility remains.   Was there once
a bridge of land from Asia to America in this region?
There is no evidence of such a link between the two
continents, for a few raised beaches indicate that
during recent geological times the Aleutian Islands
have been uplifted rather than depressed.

The passage from Asia to America at Bering
Strait, on the other hand, is comparatively easy.
The Strait itself is fifty-six miles wide, but in the
middle there are two small islands so that the
longest stretch of water is only about thirty-five

miles. Moreover the Strait is usually full of ice, which frequently becomes a solid mass from shore to shore. Therefore it would be no strange thing if some primitive savages, in hunting for seals or polar bears, crossed the Strait, even though they had no boats. Today the people on both sides of the Strait belong to the American race. They still retain traditions of a time when their ancestors crossed this narrow strip of water. The Thilanot-tines have a legend that two giants once fought fiercely on the Arctic Ocean. One would have been defeated had not a man whom he had befriended cut the tendon of his adversary's leg. The wounded giant fell into Bering Strait and formed a bridge across which the reindeer entered America. Later came a strange woman bringing iron and copper. She repeated her visits until the natives insulted her, whereupon she went underground with her fire-made treasures and came back no more. Whatever may have been the circumstances that led the earliest families to cross from Asia to America, they little recked that they had found a new continent and that they were the first of the red race.

Unless the first Americans came to the new con-tinent by way of the Kurile and Aleutian Islands,

2

it was probably their misfortune to spend many generations in the cold regions of northeastern Asia and northwestern America. Even if they reached Alaska by the Aleutian route but came to the islands by way of the northern end of the Kamchatkan Peninsula, they must have dwelt in a place where the January temperature averages − 10° F. and where there are frosts every month in the year. If they came across Bering Strait, they encountered a still more severe climate. The winters there are scarcely worse than in northern Kamchatka, but the summers are as cold as the month of March in New York or Chicago.

Perhaps a prolonged sojourn in such a climate is one reason for the stolid character of the Indians. Of course we cannot speak with certainty, but we must, in our search for an explanation, consider the conditions of life in the far north. Food is scanty at all times, and starvation is a frequent visitor, especially in winter when game is hard to get. The long periods of cold and darkness are terribly enervating. The nervous white man goes crazy if he stays too long in Alaska. Every spring the first boats returning to civilization carry an unduly large proportion of men who have lost their minds because they have endured too many dark, cold winters. His companions say of such a man, "The North has got him." Almost every Alaskan recognizes the danger. As one man said to a friend, "It is time I got out of here."

"Why?" said the friend, "you seem all right. What's the matter?"

"Well," said the other, "you see I begin to like the smell of skunk cabbage, and, when a man gets that way, it's time he went somewhere else."

The skunk cabbage, by the way, grows in Alaska in great thickets ten feet high. The man was perfectly serious, for he meant that his mind was beginning to act in ways that were not normal. Nowhere is the strain of life in the far north better described than in the poems of Robert W. Service.

Oh, the awful hush that seemed to crush me down on
    every hand,
As I blundered blind with a trail to find through that
    blank and bitter land;
Half dazed, half crazed in the winter wild, with its grim
    heart-breaking woes,
And the ruthless strife for a grip on life that only the
    sourdough knows!
North by the compass, North I pressed; river and peak
    and plain
Passed like a dream I slept to lose and waked to dream
    again.

River and plain and mighty peak — and who could
    stand unawed?
As their summits blazed, he could stand undazed at the
    foot of the throne of God.
North, aye, North, through a land accurst, shunned by
    the scouring brutes,
And all I heard was my own harsh word and the whine
    of the malamutes,
Till at last I came to a cabin squat, built in the side of a
    hill,
And I burst in the door, and there on the floor, frozen
    to death, lay Bill.[1]

The human organism inherits so delicate an ad-
justment to climate that, in spite of man's boasted
ability to live anywhere, the strain of the frozen
North eliminates the more nervous and active types
of mind.   Only those can endure whose nerves
lack sensitiveness and who are able to bear long
privation and the strain of hunger and cold and
darkness.   Though the Indian may differ from the
white man in many respects, such conditions are
probably as bad for him as for any race.   For this
reason it is not improbable that long sojourns at
way stations on the cold, Alaskan route from central Asia may have weeded out certain types of
minds.   Perhaps that is why the Indian, though

[1] From *Ballads of a Cheechako.*

brave, stoical, and hardy, does not possess the alert, nervous temperament which leads to invention and progress.

The ancestors of the red man unwittingly chose the easiest path to America and so entered the continent first, but this was their misfortune. They could not inherit the land because they chose a path whose unfavorable influence, exerted throughout centuries, left them unable to cope with later arrivals from other directions. The parts of America most favorable for the Indian are also best for the white man and Negro. There the alerter minds of the Europeans who migrated in the other direction have quickly eliminated the Indian. His long northern sojourn may be the reason why farther south in tropical lands he is even now at a disadvantage compared with the Negro or with the coolie from the East Indies. In Central America, for instance, it is generally recognized that Negroes stand the heat and moisture of the lowlands better than Indians. According to a competent authority: "The American Indians cannot bear the heat of the tropics even as well as the European, not to speak of the African race. They perspire little, their skin becomes hot, and they are easily prostrated by exertion in an elevated temperature.

They are peculiarly subject to diseases of hot climates, as hepatic disorders, showing none of the immunity of the African. Furthermore, the finest physical specimens of the race are found in the colder regions of the temperate zones, the Pampas and Patagonian Indians in the south, the Iroquois and Algonkins in the north; whereas, in the tropics they are generally undersized, short-lived, of inferior muscular force and with slight tolerance of disease."[1] "No one," adds another observer, "could live among the Indians of the Upper Amazon without being struck with their constitutional dislike to heat. The impression forced itself upon my mind that the Indian lives as a stranger or immigrant in these hot regions."[2] Thus when compared with the other inhabitants of America, from every point of view the Indian seems to be at a disadvantage, much of which may be due to the path which he took from the Old World to the New.

Before the red man lost his American heritage, he must have enjoyed it for thousands upon thousands of years. Otherwise he never could have become so different from his nearest relative, the Mongol. The two are as truly distinct races

[1] D. G. Brinton, *The American Race*, pp. 34, 35.
[2] H. W. Bates, *The Naturalist on the River Amazons*, vol. II, pp. 200, 201.

as are the white man and the Malay. Nor could the Indians themselves have become so extraordinarily diverse except during the lapse of thousands of years. The Quichua of the cold highlands of Peru is as different from the Maya of Yucatan or the Huron of southern Canada as the Swede is from the Armenian or the Jew. The separation of one stock from another has gone so far that almost countless languages have been developed. In the United States alone the Indians have fifty-five "families" of languages and in the whole of America there are nearly two hundred such groups. These comprise over one thousand distinct languages which are mutually unintelligible and at least as different as Spanish and Italian. Such differences might arise in a day at the Tower of Babel, but in the processes of evolution they take thousands of years.

During those thousands of years the red man, in spite of his Arctic handicap, by no means showed himself wholly lacking in originality and inventive ability. In Yucatan two or three thousand years ago the Mayas were such good scientists and recorded their observations of the stars so accurately that they framed a calendar more exact than any except the one that we have used for the last two centuries. They showed still greater powers of mind in inventing the art of writing and in their architecture. Later we shall depict the environment under which these things occurred; it is enough to suggest in passing that perhaps at this period the ancestors of the Indians had capacities as great as those of any people. Today they might possibly hold their own against the white man, were it not for the great handicap which they once suffered because Asia approaches America only in the cold, depressing north.

The Indians were not the only primitive people who were driven from central Asia by aridity. Another group pushed westward toward Europe. They fared far better than their Indian cousins who went to the northeast. These prospective Europeans never encountered benumbing physical conditions like those of northeastern Asia and northwestern America. Even when ice shrouded the northern part of Europe, the rest of the continent was apparently favored with a stimulating climate. Then as now, Europe was probably one of the regions where storms are most frequent. Hence it was free from the monotony which is so deadly in other regions. When the ice retreated our European ancestors doubtless followed slowly in its wake. Thus their racial character was evolved in one of the world's most stimulating regions. Privation they must have suffered, and hardihood and boldness were absolutely essential in the combat with storms, cold, wild beasts, fierce winds, and raging waves. But under the spur of constant variety and change, these difficulties were merely incentives to progress. When the time came for the people of the west of Europe to cross to America, they were of a different caliber from the previous immigrants.

Two facts of physical geography brought Europe into contact with America. One of these was the islands of the North, the other the trade-winds of the South. Each seems to have caused a preliminary contact which failed to produce important results. As in the northern Pacific, so in the northern Atlantic, islands are stepping-stones from the Old World to the New. Yet because in the latter case the islands are far apart, it is harder to cross the water from Norway and the Lofoten Islands to Iceland and Greenland than it is to cross from Asia by way of the Aleutian Islands or Bering Strait. Nevertheless in the tenth century of the Christian era bold Norse vikings made the passage in the face of storm and wind. In their slender open ships they braved the elements on voyage after voyage. We think of the vikings as pirates, and so they were. But they were also diligent colonists who tilled the ground wherever it would yield even the scantiest living. In Iceland and Greenland they must have labored mightily to carry on the farms of which the Sagas tell us. When they made their voyages, honest commerce was generally in their minds quite as much as was plunder. Leif, the son of that rough Red Eric who first settled Greenland, made a famous voyage to Vinland, the mainland of America. Like so many other voyagers he was bent on finding a region where men could live happily and on filling his boats with grapes, wood, or other commodities worth carrying home.

In view of the energy of the Norsemen, the traces of their presence in the Western Hemisphere are amazingly slight. In Greenland a few insignificant heaps of stones are supposed to show where some of them built small villages. Far in the north Stefansson found fair-haired, blue-eyed Eskimos. These may be descendants of the Norsemen, although they have migrated thousands of miles from Greenland. In Maine the Micmac Indians are said to have had a curious custom which they may have learned from the vikings. When a chief died, they chose his largest canoe. On it they piled dry wood, and on the wood they placed the body. Then they set fire to the pile and sent the blazing boat out to sea. Perhaps in earlier times the Micmacs once watched the flaming funeral pyre of a fair-haired viking. As the ruddy flames leaped skyward and were reflected in the shimmering waves of the great waters the tribesmen must have felt that the Great Spirit would gladly welcome a chief who came in such a blaze of glory. [1]

It seems strange that almost no other traces of the strong vikings are found in America. The explanation lies partly in the length and difficulty of the ocean voyage, and partly in the inhospitable character of the two great islands that served as stepping-stones from the Old World to the New. Iceland with its glaciers, storms, and long dreary winters is bad enough. Greenland is worse. Merely the tip of that island was known to the Norse — and small wonder, for then as now most of Greenland was shrouded in ice. Various Scandinavian authors, however, have thought that during the most prosperous days of the vikings the conditions in Greenland were not quite so bad as

[1] For this information I am indebted to Mr. Stansbury Hagar.

at the present day. One settlement, Osterbyden, numbered 190 farms, 12 churches, 2 monasteries, and 1 bishopric. It is even stated that apple-trees bore fruit and that some wheat was raised. "Cattle-raising and fishing," says Pettersson, "appear to have procured a good living. . . . At present the whole stock of cattle in Greenland does not amount to 100 animals."[1] In those days the ice which borders all the east coast and much of the west seems to have been less troublesome than now. In the earliest accounts nothing is said of this ice as a danger to navigation. We are told that the best sailing route was through the strait north of Cape Farewell Island, where today no ships can pass because of the ice. Since the days of the Norsemen the glaciers have increased in size, for the natives say that certain ruins are now buried beneath the ice, while elsewhere ruins can be seen which have been cut off from the rest of the country by advancing glacial tongues.

Why the Norsemen disappeared from the Western Hemisphere we do not exactly know, but there are interesting hints of an explanation. It appears

[1] O. Pettersson, *Climatic Variations in Historic and Prehistoric Times*. Svenska Hydrogrifisk — Biologiska Kommissioneur Skrifter, Haft v. Stockholm.

that the fourteenth century was a time of great distress. In Norway the crops failed year after year because of cold and storms. Provinces which were formerly able to support themselves by agriculture were obliged to import food. The people at home were no longer able to keep in touch with the struggling colony in Greenland. No supplies came from the home land, no reënforcements to strengthen the colonists and make them feel that they were a part of the great world. Moreover in the late Norse sagas much is said about the ice along the Greenland coast, which seems to have been more abundant than formerly. Even the Eskimos seem to have been causing trouble, though formerly they had been a friendly, peaceable people who lived far to the north and did not disturb the settlers. In the fourteenth century, however, they began to make raids such as are common when primitive people fall into distress. Perhaps the storms and the advancing ice drove away the seals and other animals, so that the Eskimos were left hungry. They consequently migrated south and, in the fifteenth century, finally wiped out the last of the old Norse settlers. If the Norse had established permanent settlements on the mainland of North America, they might have persisted to this day. As it was, the cold, bleak climate of the northern route across the Atlantic checked their progress. Like the Indians, they had the misfortune of finding a route to America through regions that are not good for man.

Though islands may be stepping-stones between the Old World and the New, they have not been the bringers of civilization. That function in the history of man has been left to the winds. The westerlies, however, which are the prevailing winds in the latitude of the United States and Europe, have not been of much importance. On the Atlantic side they were for many centuries a barrier to contact between the Old World and the New. On the Pacific side they have been known to blow Japanese vessels to the shores of America contrary to the will of the mariners. Perhaps the same thing may have happened in earlier times. Asia may thus have made some slight contribution to primitive America, but no important elements of civilization can be traced to this source.

From latitude 30° N. to 30° S. the trade-winds prevail. As they blow from the east, they make it easy for boats to come from Africa to America. In comparatively recent times they brought the slave ships from the Guinea coast to our Southern States.

The African, like the Indian, has passed through a most unfavorable environment on his way from central Asia to America. For ages he was doomed to live in a climate where high temperature and humidity weed out the active type of human being. Since activity like that of Europe means death in a tropical climate, the route by way of Africa has been if anything worse than by Bering Strait.

By far the most important occurrence which can be laid at the door of the trade-winds is the bringing of the civilization of Europe and the Mediterranean to the New World. Twice this may have happened, but the first occurrence is doubtful and left only a slight impress. For thousands of years the people around the Mediterranean Sea have been bold sailors. Before 600 B.C. Pharaoh Necho, so Herodotus says, had sent Phenician ships on a three-year cruise entirely around Africa. The Phenicians also sailed by way of Gibraltar to England to bring tin from Cornwall, and by 500 B.C. the Carthaginians were well acquainted with the Atlantic coast of northern Africa.

At some time or other, long before the Christian era, a ship belonging to one of the peoples of the eastern Mediterranean was probably blown to the shores of America by the steady trade-winds. Of course, no one can say positively that such a voyage occurred. Yet certain curious similarities between the Old World and the New enable us to infer with a great deal of probability that it actually happened. The mere fact, for example, that the adobe houses of the Pueblo Indians of New Mexico are strikingly like the houses of northern Africa and Persia is no proof that the civilization of the Old World and the New are related. A similar physical environment might readily cause the same type of house to be evolved in both places. When we find striking similarities of other kinds, however, the case becomes quite different. The constellations of the zodiac, for instance, are typified by twelve living creatures, such as the twins, the bull, the lion, the virgin, the crab, and the goat. Only one of the constellations, the scorpion, presents any real resemblance to the animal for which it is named. Yet the signs of the zodiac in Mediterranean lands and in pre-Columbian America from Peru to southern Mexico are almost identical. Here is a list showing the Latin and English names of the constellations and their equivalents in the calendars of the Peruvians, Mexicans, and Mayas.[1]

[1] See S. Hagar, *The Bearing of Astronomy on the Problems of the Unity or Plurality and the Probable Place of Origin of the American Aborigines*, in *American Anthropologist*, vol. xiv (1912), pp. 43–48.

Sign	English	Peruvian	Mexican	Maya
Aries	Ram	Llama	Flayer	
Taurus	Bull (originally Stag)	Stag	Stag or Deer	Stag
Gemini	Twins	Man and Woman	Twins	Two Generals
Cancer	Crab	Cuttlefish	Cuttlefish	Cuttlefish
Leo	Lion	Puma	Ocelot	Ocelot
Virgo	Virgin (Mother Goddess of Cereals)	Maize Mother	Maize Mother	Maize Mother
Libra	Scales (originally part of Scorpio)	Forks	Scorpion	Scorpion
Scorpio	Scorpion	Mummy	Scorpion	Scorpion
Sagittarius	Bowman	Arrows or Spears	Hunter and War God	Hunter and War God
Capricornus	Sea Goat	Beard	Bearded God	
Aquarius	Water Pourer	Water	Water	Water
Pisces	Fishes (and Knot)	Knot	Twisted Reeds	

Notice how closely these lists are alike. The ram does not appear in America because no such animal was known there. The nearest substitute was the llama. In the Old World the second constellation is now called the bull, but curiously enough in earlier days it was called the stag in Mesopotamia. The twins, instead of being Castor and Pollux, may equally well be a man and a woman or two generals. To landsmen not familiar with creatures of the deep, the crab and the cuttlefish would not seem greatly different. The lion is unknown in America, but the creature which most nearly takes

3

his place is the puma or ocelot. So it goes with all the signs of the zodiac. There are little differences between the Old World and the New, but they only emphasize the resemblance. Mathematically there is not one chance in thousands or even millions that such a resemblance could grow up by accident. Other similarities between ceremonies or religious words in the Old World and the New might be pointed out, but the zodiac is illustration enough.

Such resemblances, however, do not indicate a permanent connection between Mediterranean civilization and that of Central America. They do not even indicate that any one ever returned from the Western Hemisphere to the Eastern previous to Columbus. Nor do they indicate that the civilization of the New World arose from that of the Old. They simply suggest that after the people of the Mediterranean regions had become well civilized and after those of America were also sufficiently civilized to assimilate new ideas, a stray ship or two was blown by the trade-winds across the Atlantic. That hypothetical voyage was the precursor of the great journey of Columbus. Without the trade-winds this historic discoverer never could have found the West Indies. Suppose that a strong west wind had blown him backward on his course when his men were mutinous.   Suppose that he had been forced to beat against head winds week after week.   Is there one chance in a thousand that even his indomitable spirit could have kept his craft headed steadily into the west?   But because there were the trade-winds to bring him, the way was opened for the energetic people of Europe to possess the new continent.   Thus the greatest stream of immigration commenced to flow, and the New World began to take on a European aspect.

CHAPTER II

THE FORM OF THE CONTINENT

AMERICA forms the longest and straightest bone in the earth's skeleton. The skeleton consists of six great bones, which may be said to form a spheroidal tetrahedron, or pyramid with a triangular base, for when a globe with a fairly rigid surface collapses because of shrinkage, it tends to assume this form. That is what has happened to the earth. Geologists tell us that during the thousand million years, more or less, since geological history began, the earth has grown cooler and hence has contracted. Moreover some of the chemical compounds of the interior have been transformed into other compounds which occupy less space. For these reasons the earth appears to have diminished in size until now its diameter is from two hundred to four hundred miles less than formerly. During the process of contraction the crust has collapsed in four main areas, roughly triangular in shape. Between these stand the six ridges which we have called the bones. Each of the four depressed areas forms a side of our tetrahedron and is occupied by an ocean. The ridges and the areas immediately flanking the oceans form the continents. The side which we may think of as the base contains the Arctic Ocean. The ridges surrounding it are broad and flat. Large parts of them stand above sea-level and form the northern portions of North America, Europe, and Asia. A second side is the Pacific Ocean with the great ridge of the two Americas on one hand and Asia and Australia on the other. Next comes the side containing the Indian Ocean in the hollow and the ridges of Africa and Australia on either hand. The last of the four sides contains the Atlantic Ocean and is bounded by Africa and Europe on one hand and North and South America on the other. Finally the tip of the pyramid projects above the surrounding waters, and forms the continent of Antarctica.

It may seem a mere accident that this tip lies near the South Pole, while the center of the opposite face lies near the North Pole. Yet this has been of almost infinite importance in the evolution not only of plants and animals but of men. The reason is that this arrangement gives rise to a vast and almost continuous land mass in comparatively high latitudes. Only in such places does evolution appear to make rapid progress.[1]

Evolution is especially stimulated by two conditions. The first is that there shall be marked changes in the environment so that the process of natural selection has full opportunity to do its work. The second is that numerous new forms or mutants, as the biologists call them, shall be produced. Both of these conditions are most fully met in large continents in the temperate zone, for in such places climatic variations are most extreme. Such variations may take the form of extreme changes either from day to night, from season to season, or from one century to another. In any case, as Darwin long ago pointed out, they cause some forms of life to perish while others survive. Thus climatic variations are among the most powerful factors in causing natural selection and hence in stimulating evolution. Moreover it has lately been shown that variations in temperature are one of the chief causes of organic variation. Morgan and Plough,[2] for example, have discovered that

[1] W. D. Matthew, *Climate and Evolution*, N. Y. Acad. Sci., 1915.
[2] Unpublished manuscript.

when a certain fly, called the drosophila, is subjected to extremes of heat or cold, the offspring show an unusually strong tendency to differ from the parents. Hence the climatic variability of the interior of large continents in temperate latitudes provides new forms of life and then selects some of them for preservation. The fossils found in the rocks of the earth's crust support this view. They indicate that most of the great families of higher animals originated in the central part of the great land mass of Europe and Asia. A second but much smaller area of evolution was situated in the similar part of North America. From these two centers new forms of life spread outward to other continents. Their movements were helped by the fact that the tetrahedral form of the earth causes almost all the continents to be united by bridges of land.

If any one doubts the importance of the tetrahedral form, let him consider how evolution would have been hampered if the land of the globe were arranged as isolated masses in low latitudes, while oceans took the place of the present northern continents. The backwardness of the indigenous life of Africa shows how an equatorial position retards evolution. The still more marked backwardness of Australia with its kangaroos and duck-billed platypuses shows how much greater is the retardation when a continent is also small and isolated. Today, no less than in the past, the tetrahedral form of the earth and the relation of the tetrahedron to the poles and to the equator preserve the conditions that favor rapid evolution. They are the dominant factors in determining that America shall be one of the two great centers of civilization.

If North and South America be counted as one major land mass, and Europe, Asia, and Africa as another, the two present the same general features. Yet their mountains, plains, and coastal indentations are so arranged that what is on the east in one is on the west in the other. Their similarity is somewhat like that of a man's two hands placed palms down on a table.

On a map of the world place a finger of one hand on the western end of Alaska and a finger of the other on the northeastern tip of Asia and follow the main bones of the two continents. See how the chief mountain systems, the Pacific "cordilleras," trend away from one another, southeastward and southwestward. In the centers of the continents they expand into vast plateaus. That of America in the Rocky Mountain region of the United States reaches a width of over a thousand miles, while that of Asia in Tibet and western China expands to far greater proportions.

From the plateaus the two cordilleras swing abruptly Atlanticward. The Eurasian cordillera extends through the Hindu Kush, Caucasus, and Asia Minor ranges to southern Europe and the Alps. Then it passes on into Spain and ends in the volcanoes of the Canary Islands. The American cordillera swings eastward in Mexico and continues as the isolated ranges of the West Indies until it ends in the volcanoes of Martinique. Central America appears at first sight to be a continuation of the great cordillera, but really it is something quite different — a mass of volcanic material poured out in the gap where the main chain of mountains breaks down for a space. In neither hemisphere, however, is the main southward sweep of the mountains really lost. In the Old World the cordillera revives in the mountains of Syria and southern Arabia and then runs southward along the whole length of eastern Africa. In America it likewise revives in the mighty Andes, which take their rise fifteen hundred miles east of the broken end of the northern cordillera in Mexico. In the Andes even more distinctly than in Africa the cordillera forms a mighty wall running north and south. It expands into the plateau of Peru and Bolivia, just as its African compeer expands into that of Abyssinia, but this is a mere incident. The main bone, so to speak, keeps on in each case till it disappears in the great southern ocean. Even there, however, it is not wholly lost, for it revives in the cold, lofty continent of Antarctica, where it coalesces once more with the other great tetrahedral ridges of Africa and Australia.

It is easy to see that these great cordilleras have turned most of the earth's chief rivers toward the Atlantic and the Arctic Oceans. That is why these two oceans with an area of only forty-three million square miles receive the drainage from twenty million square miles of land, while the far larger Indian and Pacific Oceans with an area of ninety-one million square miles receive the rivers of only ten million square miles. The world's streams of civilization, like the rivers of water, have flowed from the great cordilleras toward the Atlantic. Half of the world's people, to be sure, are lodged in the relatively small areas known as China and India on the Pacific side of the Old World cordillera. Nevertheless the active streams of civilization have flowed mainly on the other side — the side where man apparently originated. From the earliest times the mountains have served to determine man's chief migrations. Their rugged fastnesses hinder human movements and thereby give rise to a strong tendency to move parallel to their bases. During the days of primitive man the trend of the mountains apparently directed his migrations northeastward to Bering Strait and then southeastward and southward from one end of America to the other. In the same way the migrations to Europe and Africa which ultimately reached America moved mainly parallel to the mountains.

From end to end of America the great mountains form a sharp dividing line. The aboriginal tribes on the Pacific slope are markedly different from those farther east across the mountains. Brinton sums the case up admirably:

As a rule the tribes of the western coast are not connected with any east of the mountains. What is more singular, although they differ surprisingly among themselves in language, they have marked anthropologic similarities, physical and psychical. Virchow has emphasized the fact that the skulls from the northern point of Vancouver's Island reveal an unmistakable analogy to those from the southern coast of California; and this is to a degree true of many intermediate points. Not that the crania have the same indices. On the contrary, they present great and constant differences within the same tribe; but these differences are analogous one to the other, and on fixed lines.

There are many other physical similarities which mark the Pacific Indians and contrast them with those east of the mountains. The eyes are less oblique, the nose flatter, the lips fuller, the chin more pointed, the face wider. There is more hair on the face and in the axilla, and the difference between the sexes is much more obvious.

The mental character is also in contrast. The Pacific tribes are more quiet, submissive, and docile; they have less courage, and less of that untamable independence which is so constant a feature in the history of the Algonquins and Iroquois.[1]

Although mountains may guide migrations, the plains are the regions where people dwell in greatest numbers. The plains in the two great land masses of the Old World and the New have the same inverse or right- and left-handed symmetry as the mountains. In the north the vast stretches from the Mackenzie River to the Gulf of Mexico correspond to the plains of Siberia and Russia from the Lena to the Black Sea. Both regions have a vast sweep of monotonous tundras at the north and both become fertile granaries in the center. Before the white man introduced the horse, the ox, and

[1] D. G. Brinton, *The American Race*, pp. 103-4.

iron ploughs, there prevailed an extraordinary similarity in the habits of the plains Indians from Texas
to Alberta. All alike depended on the buffalo; all
hunted him in much the same way; all used his
skins for tents and robes, his bones for tools, and
his horns for utensils. All alike made him the
center of their elaborate rituals and dances. Because the plains of North America were easy to
traverse, the relatively high culture of the ancient
people of the South spread into the Mississippi
Valley. Hence the Natchez tribe of Mississippi
had a highly developed form of sun-worship and
a well-defined caste system with three grades of
nobility in addition to the common people. Even
farther north, almost to the Ohio River, traces of
the sun-worship of Mexico had penetrated along
the easy pathway of the plains.

South of the great granaries of North America
and Eurasia the plains are broken, but occur again
in the Orinoco region of South America and the
Sahara of Africa. Thence they stretch almost unbroken toward the southern end of the continents.
In view of the fertility of the plains it is strange
that the centers of civilization have so rarely been
formed in these vast level expanses.

The most striking of the inverse resemblances

between America and the Old World are found
along the Atlantic border. In the north of Europe the White Sea corresponds to Hudson Bay
in America. Farther toward the Atlantic Ocean
Scandinavia with its mountains, glaciers, and fiords
is similar to Labrador, although more favored
because warmer. Next the islands of Great
Britain occupy a position similar to that of Newfoundland and Prince Edward Island. But here
again the eastern climate is much more favorable
than the western. Although practically all of
Newfoundland is south of England, the American
island has only six inhabitants per square mile,
while the European country has six hundred. To
the east of the British Isles the North Sea, the Bal-
tic, and Lakes Ladoga and Onega correspond in
striking fashion to the Gulf of St. Lawrence, the
river of the same name, and the Great Lakes from
Ontario to Superior. Next the indented shores
of western France and the peninsula of Spain resemble our own indented coast and the peninsula
of Florida. Here at last the American regions are
as favored as the European. Farther south the
Mediterranean and Black seas penetrate far into the interior just as does the Gulf of Mexico,
and each continent is nearly cut in two where the

canals of Suez and Panama respectively have been trenched. Finally in the southern continents a long swing eastward in America balances a similar swing westward in Africa. Thus Cape Saint Roque and Cape Verde are separated by scarcely 16° of longitude, although the extreme points of the Gulf of Mexico and the Black Sea are 140° apart. Finally to the south of the equator the continents swing away from one another once more, preserving everywhere the same curious inverse relationship.

Even more striking than the inverse resemblance of the New World to the Old is the direct similarity of North and South America. In physical form the two continents are astonishingly alike. Not only does each have the typical triangular form which would naturally arise from tetrahedral shrinking of the globe, but there are four other cardinal points of resemblance. First, in the northeast each possesses an area of extremely ancient rocks, the Laurentian highlands of Quebec and Labrador in North America and the highlands of Guiana in South America. Second, in the southeast lie highlands of old but not the most ancient rocks stretching from northeast to southwest in the Appalachian region of North America and in the Brazilian mountains of the southern continent. Third, along the western side of each continent recent crustal movements supplemented by volcanic action on a magnificent scale have given rise to a complex series of younger mountains, the two great cordilleras. Finally, the spaces between the three mountain masses are occupied by a series of vast confluent plains which in each case extend from the northern ocean to the southern and bend around the southeastern highlands. These plains are the newest part of America, for many of them have emerged from the sea only in recent geological times. Taken as a whole the resemblance between the two continents is striking.

If these four physiographic provinces of North and South America lay in similar latitudes in the respective continents we might expect each pair to have a closely similar effect on life. In fauna, flora, and even in human history they would present broad and important resemblances. As a matter of fact, however, they are as different as can well be imagined. Where North America is bathed by icy waters full of seals and floating ice South America is bathed by warm seas full of flying-fish and coral reefs. The northern continent is broadest in the cool latitudes that are most favorable for human activity. The southern expands most widely in latitudes whose debilitating monotony of heat and moisture is the worst of handicaps to human progress. The great rivers of the northern continent correspond very closely to those of the southern. The Mackenzie, however, is bound in the rigid bands of winter for eight months each year, while the Orinoco, the corresponding South American river, lies sweltering under a tropical sun which burns its grassy plains to bitter dust even as the sharp cold reduced the Mackenzie region to barren tundra. The St. Lawrence flows through fertile grain fields and the homes of an active people of the temperate zone, but the Amazon winds its slow way amid the malarious languor of vast tropical forests in which the trees shut out the sky and the few natives are apathetic with the eternal inertia of the hot, damp tropics.

Only when we come to the Mississippi in the northern continent and the Rio de la Plata in the southern do we find a pair of rivers which correspond to any degree in the character of the life surrounding them, as well as in their physiographic character. Yet even here there is a vast difference, especially in the upper courses of the river. Each at its mouth flows through a rich, fertile plain occupied

4

by a progressive, prosperous people. But the Rio de la Plata takes its rise in one of the world's most backward plains, the home of uncivilized Indians, heartless rubber adventurers, and the most rapacious of officials. Not infrequently, the degenerate white men of these regions, yielding to the subtle and insidious influence of the tropics, inflict the most outrageous abuses upon the natives, and even kill them on slight provocation. The natives in turn hate their oppressors, and when the chance comes betray them or leave them to perish in sickness and misery. The upper Mississippi, on the other hand, comes from a plain where agriculture is carried on with more labor-saving devices than are found anywhere else in the world. There States like Wisconsin and Minnesota stand in the forefront of educational and social progress. The contrasts between the corresponding rivers of the two Americas are typical of the contrasts in the history of the two continents.

CHAPTER III

THE four great physical divisions of North America — the Laurentian highland, the Appalachian highland, the plains, and the western cordillera — are strikingly different in form and structure. The Laurentian highland presents a monotonous waste of rough hills, irregular valleys, picturesque lakes, and crooked rivers. Most of it is thinly clothed with pine trees and bushes such as the blueberry and huckleberry. Yet everywhere the ancient rock crops out. No one can travel there without becoming tiresomely familiar with fine-grained, shattered schists, coarse granites, and their curiously banded relatives, the gneisses. This rocky highland stretches from a little north of the St. Lawrence River to Hudson Bay, around which it laps in the form of a V, and so is known as the Archæan V or shield.

Everywhere this oldest part of the Western

Hemisphere presents unmistakable signs of great age. The schists by their fine crumpling and scaly flakes of mineral show that they were formed deep in the bowels of the earth, for only there could they be subjected to the enormous pressure needed to transform their minerals into sheets as thin as paper. The coarse granites and gneisses proclaim still more clearly that they must have originated far down in the depths of the earth; their huge crystals of mica, quartz, hornblende, feldspar, and other minerals could never have been formed except under a blanket of rock which almost prevented the original magmas from cooling. The thousands or tens of thousands of feet of rock which once overlay the schists and still more the granites and gneisses must have been slowly removed by erosion, for there was no other way to get rid of them. This process must have taken tens of millions of years, and yet the whole work must have been practically completed a hundred or perhaps several hundred million years ago. We know this because the self-same ancient eroded surface which is exposed in the Laurentian highland is found dipping down under the oldest known fossiliferous rocks. Traces of that primitive land surface are found over a large part of the American continent.

Elsewhere they are usually buried under later strata laid down when the continent sank in part below sea-level. Only in Laurentia has the land remained steadily above the reach of the ocean throughout the millions of years.

Today this old, old land might be as rich as many others if climate had been kind to it. Its soil, to be sure, would in many parts be sandy because of the large amount of quartz in the rocks. That would be a small handicap, however, provided the soil were scores of feet deep like the red soil of the corresponding highland in the Guiana region of South America. But today the North American Laurentia has no soil worth mentioning. For some reason not yet understood this was the part of America where snow accumulated most deeply and where the largest glaciers were formed during the last great glacial period. Not once but many times its granite surface was shrouded for tens of thousands of years in ice a mile or more thick. As the ice spread outward in almost every direction, it scraped away the soil and gouged innumerable hollows in the softer parts of the underlying rock. It left the Laurentian highland a land of rocky ribs rising between clear lakes that fill the hollows. The lakes are drained by rapid rivers which wind this way and that in hopeless confusion as they strive to move seaward over the strangely uneven surface left by the ice. Such a land is good for the hunter and trapper. It is also good for the summer pleasure-seeker who would fain grow strong by paddling a canoe. For the man who would make a permanent home it is a rough, inscrutable region where one has need of more than most men's share of courage and persistence. Not only did the climate of the past cause the ice to scrape away the soil, but the climate of the present is so cold that even where new soil has accumulated the farmer can scarcely make a living.

Around the borders of the Laurentian highland the ice accomplished a work quite different from the devastation of the interior. One of its chief activities was the scouring of a series of vast hollows which now hold the world's largest series of lakes. Even the lakes of Central Africa cannot compare with our own Great Lakes and the other smaller lakes which belong to the same series. These additional lakes begin in the far north with Great Bear Lake and continue through Great Slave Lake, Lake Athabasca, and Lake Winnipeg to the Lake of the Woods, which drains into Lake Superior. All these lakes lie on the edge of the great Laurentian shield, where the ice, crowding down from the highland to the north and east, was compressed into certain already existent hollows which it widened, deepened, and left as vast bowls ready to be filled with lakes.

South and southwest of the Laurentian highland the great ice sheet proved beneficial to man. There, instead of leaving the rock naked, as in the Laurentian region, it merely smoothed off many of the irregularities of the surface and covered large areas with the most fertile soil.

In doing this, to be sure, the ice-cap scoured some hollows and left a vastly larger number of basins surrounded in whole or in part by glacial débris. These have given rise to the innumerable lakes, large and small, whose beauty so enhances the charms of Canada, New England, New York, Minnesota, and other States. They serve as reservoirs for the water supply of towns and power plants and as sources of ice and fish. Though they take land from agriculture, they probably add to the life of the community as much in other ways as they detract in this. Moreover glaciation diverted countless streams from their old courses and made them flow over falls and rapids from which water-power can easily be developed. That is one reason why glaciated New England contains over forty per cent of all the developed water-power in the United States.

Far more important, however, than the glacial lakes and rivers is the fertile glacial soil. It comes fresh from the original rocks and has not yet been exhausted by hundreds of thousands of years of weathering. It also has the advantage of being well mixed, for generally it is the product of scrapings from many kinds of rocks, each of which contributes its own particular excellence to the general composition. Take Wisconsin as an example.[1] Most parts of that State have been glaciated, but in the southwest there lies what is known as the "driftless area" because it is not covered with the "drift" or glacial débris which is thickly strewn over the rest of the State. A comparison of otherwise similar counties lying within and without the driftless area shows an astonishing contrast. In 1910 the average value of all the farm land in twenty counties covered with drift amounted to $56.90 per acre. In six counties partly covered with drift and partly driftless the value was $59.80

[1] R. H. Whitbeck, *Economic Aspects of Glaciation in Wisconsin*, in *Annals of the Association of American Geographers*, vol. III (1913), pp. 62–67.

per acre, while in thirteen counties in the driftless area it was only $33.30 per acre. In spite of the fact that glaciation causes swamps and lakes, the proportion of land cultivated in the glaciated areas is larger than in the driftless. In the glaciated area 61 per cent of the land is improved and in the driftless area only 43.5 per cent. Moreover, even though the underlying rock and the original topography be of the same kind in both cases, the average yield of crops per acre is greater where the ice has done its work. Where the country rock consists of limestone, which naturally forms a rich soil, the difference in favor of the glaciated area amounts to only 1 or 2 per cent. Where the country rock is sandy, the soil is so much improved by a mixture of fertilizing limestone or even of clay and other materials that the average yield of crops per acre in the glaciated areas is a third larger than in the driftless. Taking everything into consideration it appears that the ancient glaciation of Wisconsin increases the present agricultural output by from 20 to 40 per cent. Upwards of 10,000,000 acres of glaciated land have already been developed in the most populous parts of the State. If the average value of all products on this area is reckoned at $15 per acre and if the increased value of agricul-

tural products due to glaciation amounts to 30 per
cent, then the net value of glaciation per year to the
farmers of Wisconsin is $45,000,000. This means
about $300 for each farmer in the glaciated area.

Wisconsin is by no means unique. In Ohio, for
instance, there is also a driftless area.[1] It lies in
the southeast along the Ohio River. The difference in the value of the farm land there and in the
glaciated region is extraordinary. In the driftless
area the average value per acre in 1910 was less
than $24, while in the glaciated area it was nearly
$64. Year by year the proportion of the popula-
tion of the State in the unglaciated area is steadily
decreasing. The difference between the two parts
of the State is not due to the underlying rock structure or to the rainfall except to a slight degree.
Some of the difference is due to the fact that important cities such as Cleveland and Toledo lie on
the fertile level strip of land along the lake shore,
but this strip itself, as well as the lake, owes much
of its character to glaciation. It appears, therefore, that in Ohio, perhaps even more than in Wisconsin, man prospers most in the parts where the
ice has done its work.

    [1] William H. Hess, *The Influence of Glaciation in Ohio*, in *Bulletin of the Geographical Society of Philadelphia*, vol. xv (1917), pp. 19-42.

We have taken Wisconsin and Ohio as examples, but the effect of glaciation in those States does not differ materially from its effect all over southern Canada and the northern United States from New England to Kansas and Minnesota. Each year the people of these regions are richer by perhaps a billion dollars because the ice scraped its way down from Laurentia and spread out over the borders of the great plains on the west and of the Appalachian region on the east.

We have considered the Laurentian highland and the glaciation which centered there. Let us now turn to another highland only the northern part of which was glaciated. The Appalachian high-land, the second great division of North America, consists of three parallel bands which extend south-westward from Newfoundland and the St. Law-rence River to Georgia and Alabama. The eastern and most important band consists of hills and mountains of ancient crystalline rocks, somewhat resembling those of the Laurentian highland but by no means so old. West of this comes a broad valley eroded for the most part in the softer por-tions of a highly folded series of sedimentary rocks which are of great age but younger than the

crystalline rocks to the east.   The third band is the
Alleghany plateau, composed of almost horizontal
rocks which lie so high and have been so deeply
dissected that they are often called mountains.

The three Appalachian bands by no means preserve a uniform character throughout their entire
length.   The eastern crystalline band has its chief
development in the northeast.   There it com-
prises the whole of New England and a large part
of the maritime provinces of Canada as well as
Newfoundland.   Its broad development in New
England causes that region to be one of the most
clearly defined natural units of the United States.
Ancient igneous rocks such as granite lie intricately
mingled with old and highly metamorphosed sedi-
ments.   Since some of the rocks are hard and others
soft and since all have been exposed to extremely
long erosion, the topography of New England consists typically of irregular masses of rounded hills
free from precipices.   Here and there hard masses
of unusually resistant rock stand up as isolated
rounded heights, like Mount Katahdin in Maine.
They are known as "monadnocks" from the mountain of that name in southern New Hampshire.   In
other places larger and more irregular masses of
hard rock form mountain groups like the White

Mountains, the Green Mountains, and the Berk-
shires, each of which is merely a great series of
monadnocks.

In the latitude of southern New York the crystalline rocks are compressed into narrow compass
and lose their mountainous character. They form
the irregular hills on which New York City itself
is built and which make the suburbs of Westchester
County along the eastern Hudson so diverse and
beautiful. To the southeast the topography of the
old crystalline band becomes still less pronounced,
as may be seen in the rolling, fertile hills around
Philadelphia. Farther south the band divides into
two parts, the mountains proper and the Piedmont
plateau. The mountains begin at the Blue Ridge,
which in Virginia raises its even-topped heights
mile after mile across the length of that State. In
North Carolina, however, they lose their character
as a single ridge and expand into the broad mass of
the southern Appalachians. There Mount Mitch-
ell dominates the eastern part of the American
continent and is surrounded by over thirty other
mountains rising to a height of at least six thousand
feet. The Piedmont plateau, which lies at the
eastern foot of the Blue Ridge, is not really a
plateau but a peneplain or ancient lowland worn

almost to a plain. It expands to a width of one hundred miles in Virginia and the Carolinas and forms the part of those States where most of the larger towns are situated. Among its low gentle heights there rises an occasional little monadnock like Chapel Hill, where the University of North Carolina lies on a rugged eminence which strikingly recalls New England. For the most part, however, the hills of the Piedmont region are lower and more rounded than those in the neighborhood of Philadelphia. The country thus formed has many advantages, for it is flat enough to be used for agriculture and yet varied enough to be free from the monotony of the level plains.

The prolonged and broken inner valley forming the second band of the Appalachians was of some importance as a highway in the days of the Indians. Today the main highways of traffic touch it only to cross it as quickly as possible. From Lake Champlain it trends straight southward in the Hudson Valley until the Catskills have been passed. Then, while the railroads and all the traffic go on down the gorge of the Hudson to New York, the valley swings off into Pennsylvania past Scranton, Wilkesbarre, and Harrisburg. There the underlying rock consists of a series of alternately hard and soft layers which have been crumpled up much as one might wrinkle a rug with one's foot. The pressure involved in the process changed and hardened the rocks so much that the coal which they contain was converted into anthracite, the finest coal in all the world and the only example of its kind. Even the famous Welsh coal has not been so thoroughly hardened. During a long period of erosion the tops of the folded layers were worn off to a depth of thousands of feet and the whole country was converted into an almost level plain. Then in the late geological period known as the early Tertiary the land was lifted up again, and once more erosion went on. The soft rocks were thus etched away until broad valleys were formed. The hard layers were left as a bewildering succession of ridges with flat tops. A single ridge may double back and forth so often that the region well deserves the old Indian name of the "Endless Mountains." Southwestward the valley grows narrower, and the ridges which break its surface become straighter. Everywhere they are flat-topped, steep-sided, and narrow, while between them lie parts of the main valley floor, flat and fertile. Here in the south, even more clearly than in the north, the valley is bordered on the east by the sharply upstanding range of the crystalline Appalachians, while on the west with equal regularity it comes to an end in an escarpment which rises to the Alleghany plateau.

This plateau, the third great band of the Appalachians, begins on the south side of the Mohawk Valley. To the north its place is taken by the Adirondacks, which are an outlier of the great Laurentian area of Canada. The fact that the outlier and the plateau are separated by the low strip of the Mohawk Valley makes this the one place where the highly complex Appalachian system can easily be crossed. If the Alleghany plateau joined the Adirondacks, Philadelphia instead of New York would be the greatest city of America. Where the plateau first rises on the south side of the Mohawk, it attains heights of four thousand feet in the Catskill Mountains. We think of the Catskills as mountains, but their steep cliffs and table-topped heights show that they are really the remnants of a plateau, the nearly horizontal strata of which have not yet been worn away. Westward from the Catskills the plateau continues through central New York to western Pennsylvania. Those who have traveled on the Pennsylvania Railroad may remember how the railroad climbs the escarpment at Altoona. Farther east the train has passed alternately through gorges cut in the parallel ridges and through fertile open valleys forming the main floor of the inner valley. Then it winds up the long ascent of the Alleghany front in a splendid horseshoe curve. At the top, after a short tunnel, the train emerges in a wholly different country. The valleys are without order or system. They wind this way and that. The hills are not long ridges but isolated bits left between the winding valleys. Here and there beds of coal blacken the surface, for here we are among the rocks from which the world's largest coal supply is derived. Since the layers lie horizontally and have never been compressed, the same material which in the inner valley has been changed to hard, clean-burning anthracite here remains soft and smoky.

In its southwestern continuation through West Virginia and Kentucky to Tennessee the plateau maintains many of its Pennsylvanian characteristics, but it now rises higher and becomes more inaccessible. The only habitable portions are the bottoms of the valleys, but they are only wide enough to support a most scanty population. Between them most of the land is too rough for anything except forests. Hence the people who live at the bottoms of the valleys are strangely isolated.

They see little or nothing of the world at large or even of their neighbors. The roads are so few and the trails so difficult that the farmers cannot easily take their produce to market. Their only recourse has been to convert their bulky corn into whisky, which occupied little space in proportion to its value. Since the mountaineer has no other means of getting ready money, it is not strange that he has become a moonshiner and has fought bitterly for what he genuinely believed to be his rights in that occupation. Education has not prospered on the plateau because the narrowness of the valleys causes the population to be too poor and too scattered to support schools. For the same reason feuds grow up. When people live by themselves they become suspicious. Not being used to dealing with their neighbors, they suspect the motives of all but their intimate friends. Moreover, in those deep valleys, with their steep sides and their general inaccessibility, laws cannot easily be enforced, and therefore each family takes the law into its own hands.

Today the more rugged parts of the Appalachian system are chiefly important as a hindrance to communication. On the Atlantic slope of the old crystalline band there are great areas of gentle relief where an abundant population can dwell.

Westward on the edges of the plateau and the plains beyond a still greater population can find a living, but in the intervening space there is opportunity for only a few. The great problem is to cross the mountains as easily as possible. Each accessible crossing-place is associated with a city. Boston, as well as New York, owes much to the low Mohawk-Hudson route, but is badly handicapped because it has no easy means of crossing the eastern crystalline band. Philadelphia, on the other hand, benefits from the fact that in its vicinity the crystallines are low and can readily be crossed even without the aid of the valleys of the Delaware and Schuylkill rivers. It is handicapped, however, by the Alleghany escarpment at Altoona, even though this is lower there than farther south. Baltimore, in the same way, owes much of its growth to the easy pathways of the Susquehanna on the north and the Potomac on the south. Farther south both the crystalline band and the Alleghany plateau become more difficult to traverse, so that communication between the Atlantic coast and the Mississippi Valley is reduced to small proportions. Happy is New York in its situation where no one of the three bands of the Appalachians opposes any obstacle.

The plains of North America form the third of the four main physical divisions of the continent. For the most part they lie between the great western cordillera on one side and the Laurentian and Appalachian highlands on the other. Yet they lap around the southern end of the Appalachians and run far up the Atlantic coast to New York. They remained beneath the sea till a late date, much later than the other three divisions. They were not, however, covered with deep water like that of the abysmal oceans, but only with shallow seas from which the land at times emerged. In spite of the old belief to the contrary, the continents appear to be so permanent that they have occupied practically their present positions from the remotest geological times. They have moved slowly up and down, however, so that some parts have frequently been submerged, and the plains are the parts that remained longest under water.

The plains of North America may be divided into four parts according to the character of their surface: the Atlantic coastal plain, the prairies, the northwestern peneplain, and the southwestern high plains. The Atlantic coastal plain lies along the Atlantic coast from New York southward to Florida and Alabama. It also forms a great embayment up the Mississippi Valley as far as the Ohio River, and it extends along the shore of the Gulf of Mexico to the Rio Grande. The chief characteristic of this Atlantic and Gulf coastal plain is its belted nature. One layer of rocks is sandy, another consists of limestone, and a third of clay. When uplifted and eroded each assumes its own special topography and is covered with its own special type of vegetation. Thus in South Carolina and Georgia the crystalline Piedmont band of the Appalachian province is bordered on the southeast by a belt of sandstone. This rock is so far from the sea and has been raised so high above it that erosion has converted it into a region of gentle hills, whose tops are six hundred or seven hundred feet above sea-level. Its sandy soil is so poor that farming is difficult. The hills are largely covered with pine, yielding tar and turpentine. Farther seaward comes a broad band of younger rock which forms a clayey soil or else a yellow sandy loam. These soils are so rich that splendid cotton crops can be raised, and hence the region is thickly populated. Again there comes a belt of sand, the so-called "pine barrens," which form a poor section about fifty miles inland from the coast. Finally the coastal belt itself has emerged from beneath the sea so recently and lies so nearly at sea-level that it has not been greatly eroded, and is still covered with numerous marshes and swamps. The rich soil and the moisture are good for rice, but the region is so unhealthy and so hard to drain that only small parts are inhabited.

Everywhere in the coastal plain this same belted character is more or less evident. It has much to do with all sorts of activities from farming to politics. On consulting the map showing the cotton production of the United States in 1914, one notices the two dark bands in the southeast. One of them, extending from the northwestern part of South Carolina across Georgia and Alabama, is due to the fertile soil of the Piedmont region. The other, lying nearer the sea, begins in North Carolina and extends well into Alabama before it swings around to the northwest toward the area of heavy production along the Mississippi. It is due to the fertile soil of that part of the coastal plain known as the "cotton belt." Portions of it are called the "black belt," not because of the colored population, but because of the darkness of the soil. Since this land has always been prosperous, it has regularly been conservative in politics.

The Atlantic coastal plain is by no means the

only part of the United States where the fertility of the soil is the dominant fact in the life of the people. Because of their rich soil the prairies which extend from western Ohio to the Missouri River and northward into Canada are fast becoming the most steadily prosperous part of America. They owe their surpassing richness largely to glaciation. We have already seen how the coming of the ice-sheet benefited the regions on the borders of the old Laurentian highland. This same benefit extended over practically the whole of what are now the prairies. Before the advent of the ice the whole section consisted of a broadly banded coastal plain much older than that of the Atlantic coast. When the ice with its burden of material scraped from the hills of the north passed over the coastal plain, it filled the hollows with rich new soil. The icy streams that flowed out from the glaciers were full of fine sediment, which they deposited over enormous flood plains. During dry seasons the winds picked up this dust and spread it out still more widely, forming the great banks of yellow loess whose fertile soil mantles the sides of many a valley in the Mississippi basin. Thus glaciers, streams, and winds laid down ten, twenty, fifty, or even one hundred feet of the finest, most fertile soil.

We have already seen how much the soil was
improved by glaciation in Wisconsin and Ohio.
It was in the prairie States that this improvement
reached a maximum. The soil there is not only
fine grained and free from rocks, but it consists of
particles brought from widely different sources and
is therefore full of all kinds of plant foods. In most
parts of the world a fine-grained soil is formed only
after a prolonged period of weathering which
leaches out many valuable chemical elements. In
the prairies, however, the soil consists largely of
materials that were mechanically ground to dust
by the ice without being exposed to the action of
weathering. Thus they have reached their present
resting-places without the loss of any of their original plant foods. When such a soil is found with a
climate which is good for crops and which is also
highly stimulating to man, the combination is almost ideal. There is some justification for those
who say that the north central portion of the
United States is more fortunate than any other
part of the earth. Nowhere else, unless in western Europe, is there such a combination of fertile
soil, fine climate, easy communication, and possibilities for manufacturing and commerce. Iron
from that outlier of the Laurentian highland which

forms the peninsula of northern Michigan can easily be brought by water almost to the center of the prairie region. Coal in vast quantities lies directly under the surface of this region, for the rock of the ancient coastal plain belongs to the same Pennsylvanian series which yields most of the world's coal. Here man is, indeed, blessed with resources and opportunities scarcely equaled in any other part of the world, and finds the only drawbacks to be the extremes of temperature in both winter and summer and the remoteness of the region from the sea. Because of the richness of their heritage and because they live safely protected from threats of foreign aggression, the people who live in this part of the world are in danger of being slow to feel the currents of great world movements.

The western half of the plains of North America consists of two parts unlike either the Atlantic coastal plain or the prairies. From South Dakota and Nebraska northward far into Canada and westward to the Rocky Mountains there extends an ancient peneplain worn down to gentle relief by the erosion of millions of years. It is not so level as the plains farther east nor so low. Its western margin reaches heights of four or five thousand feet. Here and there, especially on the western side, it rises to the crest of a rugged escarpment where some resistant layer of rocks still holds itself up against the forces of erosion. Elsewhere its smooth surfaces are broken by lava-capped mesas or by ridges where some ancient volcanic dike is so hard that it has not yet been worn away. The soil, though excellent, is thinner and less fertile than in the prairies. Nevertheless the population might in time become as dense and prosperous as almost any in the world if only the rainfall were more abundant and good supplies of coal were not quite so far away. Yet in spite of these handicaps the northwestern peneplain with its vast open stretches, its cattle, its wheat, and its opportunities is a most attractive land.

South of Nebraska and Wyoming the "high plains," the last of the four great divisions of the plains, extend as far as western Texas. These, like the prairies, have been built up by deposits brought from other regions. In this case, however, the deposits consist of gravel, sand, and silt which the rivers have gradually washed out from the Rocky Mountains. As the rivers have changed their courses from one bed to another, layer after layer has been laid down to form a vast plain like a gently sloping beach hundreds of miles wide. In most places the streams are no longer building this up. Frequently they have carved narrow valleys hundreds of feet deep in the materials which they formerly deposited. Elsewhere, however, as in western Kansas, most of the country is so flat that the horizon is like that of the ocean. It seems almost incredible that at heights of four or five thousand feet the plains can still be so wonderfully level. When the grass is green, when the spring flowers are at their best, it would be hard to find a picture of greater beauty. Here the buffalo wandered in the days before the white man destroyed them. Here today is the great cattle region of America. Here is the region where the soul of man is filled with the feeling of infinite space.

To the student of land forms there is an ever-present contrast between those due directly to the processes which build up the earth's surface and those due to the erosive forces which destroy what the others have built. In the great plains of North America two of the divisions, that is, the Atlantic coastal plain of the southeast and the peneplain of the northwest, owe their present form to the forces of erosion. The other two, that is, the prairies and the high plains, still bear the impress of the original processes of deposition and have been modified to only a slight extent by erosion.

A similar but greater contrast separates the mountains of eastern North America and those of the western cordillera — the fourth and last of the main physical divisions of the continent. In both the Laurentian and the Appalachian highlands the eastern mountains show no trace of the original forms produced by the faulting of the crust or by volcanic movements. All the original distinctive topography has been removed. What we see to-day is the product of erosion working upon rocks that were thousands of feet beneath the surface when they were brought to their present positions. In the western cordillera, on the contrary, although much of the present form of the land is due to erosion, a vast amount is due directly to so-called "tectonic" activities such as the breaking of the crust, the pouring out of molten lavas, and the bursting forth of explosive eruptions.

The character of these tectonic activities has differed widely in different parts of the cordillera. A broad upheaval of great blocks of the earth's crust without tilting or disturbance has produced the plateaus of Arizona and Utah. The gorges that have been rapidly cut into such great upheaved blocks form part of the world's most striking scenery. The Grand Canyon of the Colorado with its tremendous platforms, mesas, and awe-inspiring cliffs could have been formed in no other way. Equally wonderful are some of the narrow canyons in the broadly upheaved plateaus of southern Utah where the tributaries of the Virgin and other rivers have cut red or white chasms thousands of feet deep and so narrow that at their bottoms perpetual twilight reigns. It is a curious proof of the fallibility of human judgment that these great gorges are often cited as the most striking examples of the power of erosion. Wonderful as these gorges certainly are, the Piedmont plain or the northwestern peneplain is far more wonderful. Those regions had their grand canyons once upon a time, but now erosion has gone so far that it has reduced the whole area to the level of the bottoms of the gorges. Though such a fate is in store for all the marvelous scenery of the western cordillera, we have it, for the present at least, as one of the most stimulating panoramas of our American environment. No man worthy of the name can sit on the brink of a great canyon or gaze up from the dark depths of a gorge without a sense of awe and wonder. There, as in few other places, Nature shows with unmistakable grandeur the marvelous power and certainty with which her laws work out the destiny of the universe.

In other parts of the great American cordillera some of the simplest and youngest mountain ridges in the world are found. In southern Oregon, for example, lava blocks have been broken and uplifted and now stand with steep fresh faces on one side and with the old surface inclining more gently on the other. Tilted blocks on a larger scale and much more deeply carved by erosion are found in the lofty St. Elias Mountain of Alaska, where much of the erosion has been done by some of the world's greatest glaciers. The western slope of the Wasatch Mountains facing the desert of Utah is the wall of a huge fracture, as is the eastern face of the Sierra Nevadas facing the deserts of Nevada. Each of these great faces has been deeply eroded. At the base, however, recent breaking and upheaval of the crust have given rise to fresh uneroded slopes. Some take the form of triangular facets, where a series of ridges has been sliced across and lifted up by a great fault. Others assume the shape of terraces which sometimes continue along the base of the mountains for scores of miles. In places they seem like bluffs cut by an ancient lake, but suddenly they change their altitude or pass from one drainage area to another as no lake-formed strand could possibly do.

In other parts of the cordillera, mountains have been formed by a single arching of the crust without any breaking. Such is the case in the Uinta Mountains of northwestern Utah and in some of the ranges of the Rocky Mountains in Colorado. The Black Hills of South Dakota, although lying out in the plains, are an example of the same kind of structure and really belong to the cordillera. In them the layers of the earth's crust have been bent up in the form of a great dome. The dome structure, to be sure, has now been largely destroyed, for erosion has long been active. The result is that the harder strata form a series of concentric ridges, while between them are ring-shaped valleys, one of which is so level and unbroken that it is known to the Indians as the "race-course." In other parts of the cordillera great masses of rock have been pushed horizontally upon the tops of others. In Montana, for example, the strata of the plains have been bent down and overridden by those of the mountains. These are only a few of the countless forms of breaking, faulting, and crumpling which have given to the cordillera an almost infinite variety of scenery.

The work of mountain building is still active in the western cordillera, as is evident from such an event as the San Francisco earthquake. In the Owens Valley region in southern California the gravelly beaches of old lakes are rent by fissures made within a few years by earthquakes. In other places fresh terraces on the sides of the valley mark the lines of recent earth movements, while newly formed lakes lie in troughs at their base. These Owens Valley movements of the crust are parts of the stupendous uplift which has raised the Sierra Nevada to heights of over 14,000 feet a few miles to the west. Along the fault line at the base of the mountains there runs for over 250 miles the world's longest aqueduct, which was built to relieve Los Angeles from the danger of drought. It is a strange irony of fate that so delicate and so vital an artery of civilization should be forced to lie where a renewal of earthquake movements may break it at any time. Yet there was no other place to put it, for in spite of man's growing control of nature he was forced to follow the topography of the region in which he lived and labored.

On the southern side of the Mohave Desert a

little to the east of where the Los Angeles aqueduct crosses the mountains in its southward course, the record of an earthquake is preserved in unique fashion. The steep face of a terrace is covered with trees forty or fifty years old. Near the base the trees are bent in peculiar fashion. Their lower portions stand at right angles to the steeply sloping face of the terrace, but after a few feet the trunks bend upward and stand vertically. Clearly when these trees were young the terrace was not there. Then an earthquake came. One block of the earth's crust was dropped down while another was raised up. Along the dividing line a terrace was formed. The trees that happened to stand along the line were tilted and left in a slanting position on the sloping surface between the two parts of the earth's crust. They saw no reason to stop growing, but, turning their tips toward the sky, they bravely pushed upward. Thus they preserve in a striking way the record of this recent movement of the earth's crust.

Volcanoes as well as earth movements have occurred on a grand scale within a few hundred years in the cordillera. Even where there is to-day no visible volcanic activity, recent eruptions have left traces as fresh as if they had occurred but

6

yesterday. On the borders of the Grand Canyon of the Colorado one can see not only fresh cones of volcanic ash but lava which has poured over the edges of the cliffs and hardened while in the act of flowing. From Orizaba and Popocatepetl in Mexico through Mount San Francisco in Arizona, Lassen Peak and Mount Shasta in California, Mount Rainier with its glaciers in the Cascade Range of Washington, and Mount Wrangell in Alaska, the cordillera contains an almost unbroken chain of great volcanoes. All are either active at present or have been active within very recent times. In 1912 Mount Katmai, near the northwestern end of the volcanic chain, erupted so violently that it sent dust around the whole world. The presence of the dust caused brilliant sunsets second only to those due to Krakatoa in 1883. It also cut off so much sunlight that the effect was felt in measurements made by the Smithsonian Institution in the French provinces of North Africa. In earlier times, throughout the length of the cordillera great masses of volcanic material were poured out to form high plateaus like those of southern Mexico or of the Columbia River in Oregon. In Utah some of these have been lifted up so that heavy caps of lava now form isolated sheets topping lofty plateaus. There the lowland shepherds drive their sheep in summer and live in absolute isolation for months at a time. There, as everywhere, the cordillera bears the marks of mountains in the making, while the mountains of eastern America bear the marks of those that were made when the world was young.

The geysers and hot springs of the Yellowstone are another proof of recent volcanic activity. They owe their existence to hot rocks which lie only a little way below the surface and which not long ago were molten lava. The terraces and platforms built by the geysers are another evidence that the cordillera is a region where the surface of the earth is still being shaped into new forms by forces acting from within. The physical features of the country are still in process of construction.

In spite of the importance of the constructive forces which are still building up the mountains, much of the finest scenery of the cordillera is due to the destructive forces of erosion. The majestic Columbia Canyon, like others of its kind, is the work of running water. Glaciers also have done their part. During the glacial period the forces which control the paths of storms did not give to the cordillera region such an abundance of snow

as was sifted down upon Laurentia. Therefore
no such huge continental glaciers have flowed
out over millions of square miles of lower country.
Nevertheless among the mountains themselves the
ice gouged and scraped and smoothed and at its
lower edges deposited great moraines. Its work today makes the cliffs and falls of the Yosemite one
of the world's most famous bits of scenery. This
scenery is young and its beauty will pass in a short
time as geology counts the years, for in natural
scenery as in human life it is youth that makes
beauty. The canyons, waterfalls, and geysers of
the cordillera share their youth with the lakes,
waterfalls, and rapids due to recent glaciation in
the east. Nevertheless, though youth is the condition of most striking beauty, maturity and old
age are the condition of greatest usefulness. The
young cordillera with its mountains still in the making can support only a scanty population, whereas
the old eastern mountains, with the lines of long
life engraved upon every feature, open their arms
to man and let him live and prosper.

It is not enough that we should picture merely
the four divisions of the land of our continent.
We must see how the land meets the sea. In low

latitudes in both the Old World and the New, the continents have tended to emerge farther and farther from the sea during recent geological times. Hence on the eastern side of both North and South America from New Jersey to Brazil the ocean is bordered for the most part by coastal plains, uplifted from the sea only a short time ago. On the mountainous western side of both continents, however, the sea bottom shelves downward so steeply that its emergence does not give rise to a plain but merely to a steep slope on which lie a series of old beaches several hundred and even one thousand feet above the present shore line. Such conditions are not favorable to human progress. The coastal plains produced by uplift of the land may be fertile and may furnish happy homes for man, but they do not permit ready access to the sea because they have no harbors. The chief harbor of Mexico at Vera Cruz is merely a little nick in the coast-line and could never protect a great fleet, even with the help of its breakwater. Where an enterprising city like Los Angeles lies on the uplifted Pacific coast, it must spend millions in wresting a harbor from the very jaws of the sea.

In high latitudes in all parts of the world the land has recently been submerged beneath the sea.

In some places, especially those like the coasts of Virginia and central California which lie in middle latitudes, a recent slight submergence has succeeded a previous large emergence. Wherever such sinking of the land has taken place, it has given rise to countless bays, gulfs, capes, islands, and fiords. The ocean water has entered the valleys and has drowned their lower parts. It has surrounded the bases of hills and left them as islands; it has covered low valleys and has created long sounds where traffic may pass with safety even in great storms. Though much land has thus been lost which would be good for agriculture, commerce has been wonderfully stimulated. Through Long Island Sound there pass each day hundreds of boats which again and again would suffer distress and loss if they were not protected from the open sea. It is no accident that of the eight largest metropolitan districts in the United States five have grown up on the shores of deep inlets which are due to the drowning of valleys.

Nor must the value of scenery be forgotten in a survey such as this. Year by year we are learning that in this restless, strenuous American life of ours vacations are essential. We are learning, too, that the love of beauty is one of Nature's greatest healers.   Regions like the coast of Maine and Puget Sound, where rugged land and life-giving ocean interlock, are worth untold millions because of their inspiring beauty.   It is indeed marvelous that in the latitude of the northern United States and southern Canada so many circumstances favorable to human happiness are combined.   Fertile soil, level plains, easy passage across the mountains, coal, iron, and other metals imbedded in the rocks, and a stimulating climate, all shower their blessings upon man.   And with all these blessings goes the advantage of a coast which welcomes the mariner and brings the stimulus of foreign lands, while at the same time it affords rest and inspiration to the toilers here at home.

CHAPTER IV

THE GARMENT OF VEGETATION

No part of the world can be truly understood without a knowledge of its garment of vegetation, for this determines not only the nature of the animal inhabitants but also the occupations of the majority of human beings. Although the soil has much to do with the character of vegetation, climate has infinitely more. It is temperature which causes the moss and lichens of the barren tundras in the far north to be replaced by orchids, twining vines, and mahogany trees near the equator. It is rainfall which determines that vigorous forests shall grow in the Appalachians in latitudes where grass-lands prevail in the plains and deserts in the western cordillera.

Forests, grass-lands, deserts, represent the three chief types of vegetation on the surface of the earth. Each is a response to certain well-defined conditions of climate. Forests demand an abundance of

moisture throughout the entire season of growth.
Where this season lasts only three months the
forest is very different from where it lasts twelve.
But no forest can be vigorous if the ground habitu-
ally becomes dry for a considerable period during
which the weather is warm enough for growth.
Desert vegetation, on the other hand, which
consists primarily of bushes with small, drought-
resistant leaves, needs only a few irregular and in-
frequent showers in order to endure long periods
of heat and drought. Discontinuity of moisture
is the cause of deserts, just as continuity is the
necessary condition of forest growth. Grasses prevail where the climatic conditions are intermediate
between those of the forest and the desert. Their
primary requisite is a short period of fairly abundant moisture with warmth enough to ripen their
seeds. Unlike the trees of the forests, they thrive
even though the wet period be only a fraction of
the entire time that is warm enough for growth.
Unlike the bushes of the desert, they rarely thrive
unless the ground is well soaked for at least a
few weeks.

Most people think of forests as offering far more
variety than either deserts or grass-lands. To them
grass is just grass, while trees seem to possess

individuality. In reality, however, the short turfy
grass of the far north differs from the four-foot
fronds of the bunchy saccaton grass of Arizona,
and from the far taller tufts of the plumed pampas
grass, much more than the pine tree differs from the
palm. Deserts vary even more than either forests
or grass-lands. The traveler in the Arizona desert,
for example, has been jogging across a gravelly
plain studded at intervals of a few yards with little
bushes a foot high. The scenery is so monotonous
and the noon sunshine so warm that he almost falls
asleep. When he wakes from his day-dream, so
weird are his surroundings that he thinks he must
be in one of the places to which Sindbad was carried by the roc. The trail has entered an open
forest of joshuas, as the big tree yuccas are called
in Arizona. Their shaggy trunks and uncouth
branches are rendered doubly unkempt by sword-
like, ashy-yellow dead leaves that double back on
the trunk but refuse to fall to the ground. At a
height of from twelve to twenty feet each arm of
the many-branched candelabrum ends in a stiff ro-
sette of gray-green spiky leaves as tough as hemp.
Equally bizarre and much more imposing is a desert "stand" of giant suhuaros, great fluted tree-
cacti thirty feet or more high. In spite of their

size the suhuaros are desert types as truly as is sagebrush.

In America the most widespread type of forest is the evergreen coniferous woodland of the north. Its pines, firs, spruces, hemlocks, and cedars which are really junipers, cover most of Canada together with northern New England and the region south of Lakes Huron and Superior. At its northern limit the forest looks thoroughly forlorn. The gnarled and stunted trees are thickly studded with half-dead branches bent down by the weight of snow, so that the lower ones sweep the ground, while the upper look tired and discouraged from their struggle with an inclement climate. Farther south, however, the forest loses this aspect of terrific struggle. In Maine, for example, it gives a pleasant impression of comfortable prosperity. Wherever the trees have room to grow, they are full and stocky, and even where they are crowded together their slender upspringing trunks look alert and energetic. The signs of death and decay, indeed, appear everywhere in fallen trunks, dead branches, and decayed masses of wood, but moss and lichens, twinflowers and bunchberries so quickly mantle the prostrate trees that they do not seem like tokens of weakness. Then, too, in every open space thousands of young trees bank their soft green masses so gracefully that one has an ever-present sense of pleased surprise as he comes upon this younger foliage out of the dim aisles among the bigger trees.

Except on their southern borders the great northern forests are not good as a permanent home for man. The snow lies so late in the spring and the summers are so short and cool that agriculture does not prosper. As a home for the fox, marten, weasel, beaver, and many other fur-bearing animals, however, the coniferous forests are almost ideal. That is why the Hudson's Bay Company is one of the few great organizations which have persisted and prospered from colonial times to the present. As long ago as 1670 Charles II granted to Prince Rupert and seventeen noblemen and gentlemen a charter so sweeping that, aside from their own powers of assimilation, there was almost no limit to what the "Governor and Company of Adventurers of England trading into Hudson's Bay" might acquire. By 1749, nearly eighty years after the granting of the charter, however, the Company had only four or five forts on the coast of Hudson Bay, with about 120 regular employees. Nevertheless the poor Indians were so ignorant of the value of their furs and the consequent profits were so large that, after Canada had been ceded to Great Britain in 1763, a rival organization, the Northwest Fur Company of Montreal, was established. Then there began an era that was truly terrible for the Indians of the northern forest. In their eagerness to get the valuable furs the companies offered the Indians strong liquors in an abundance that ruined the poor red man, body and soul. Moreover the fur-bearing animals were killed not only in winter but during the breeding season. Many mother animals were shot and their little ones were left to die. Hence in a short time the wild creatures of the great northern forest were so scarce that the Indians well-nigh starved.

In spite of this slaughter of fur-bearing animals, the same Company still draws fat dividends from the northern forest and its furry inhabitants. If the forest had been more habitable, it would long ago have been occupied by settlers, as have its warmer, southern portions, and the Company would have ceased to exist. Aside from the regions too cold or too dry to support any vegetation whatever, few parts of the world are more deadening to civilization than the forests of the far north. Near the northern limit of the great evergreen forest of North America wild animals are so rare that a family of hunting Indians can scarcely find a living in a thousand square miles. Today the voracious maw of the daily newspaper is eating the spruce and hemlock by means of relentless saws and rattling pulp-mills. In the wake of the lumbermen settlers are tardily spreading northward from the more favored tracts in northern New England and southern Canada. Nevertheless most of the evergreen forests of the north must always remain the home of wild animals and trappers, a backward region in which it is easy for a great fur company to maintain a practical monopoly.

Outliers of the pine forest extend far down into the United States. The easternmost lies in part along the Appalachians and in part along the coastal plain from southern New Jersey to Texas. The coastal forest is unlike the other coniferous forests in two respects, for its distribution and growth are not limited by long winters but by sandy soil which quickly becomes dry. This drier southern pine forest lacks the beauty of its northern companion. Its trees are often tall and stately, but they are usually much scattered and are surrounded by stretches of scanty grass. There is no

trace of the mossy carpet and dense copses of under-
growth that add so much to the picturesqueness of
the forests farther north. The unkempt half-breed
or Indian hunter is replaced by the prosaic gatherer
of turpentine. As the man of the southern forests
shuffles along in blue or khaki overalls and carries
his buckets from tree to tree, he seems a dull figure
contrasted with the active northern hunter who
glides swiftly and silently from trap to trap on his
rawhide snowshoes. Yet though the southern pine
forest may be less picturesque than the northern,
it is more useful to man.   In spite of its sandy soil,
much of this forest land is being reclaimed, and all
will some day probably be covered by farms.

Two other outliers of the northern evergreen
forest extend southward along the cool heights of
the Rocky Mountains and of the Pacific coast
ranges of the United States. In the Olympic and
Sierra Nevada ranges the most western outlier of
this northern band of vegetation probably contains
the most inspiring forests of the world. There grow
the vigorous Oregon pines, firs, and spruces, and
the still more famous Big Trees or sequoias. High
on the sides of the Sierra above the yuccas, the
live oaks, and the deciduous forest of the lower
slopes, one meets these Big Trees. To come upon

them suddenly after a long, rough tramp over the sunny lower slopes is the experience of a lifetime. Upward the great trees rise sheer one hundred feet without a branch. The huge fluted trunks encased in soft, red bark six inches or a foot thick are more impressive than the columns of the grandest cathedral. It seems irreverent to speak above a whisper. Each tree is a new wonder. One has to walk around it and study it to appreciate its enormous size. Where a tree chances to stand isolated so that one can see its full majesty, the sense of awe is tempered by the feeling that in spite of their size the trees have a beauty all their own. Lifted to such heights, the branches appear to be covered with masses of peculiarly soft and rounded foliage like the piled-up banks of a white cumulus cloud before a thunderstorm. At the base of such a tree the eye is caught by the sharp, triangular outline of one of its young progeny. The lower branches sweep the ground. The foliage is harsh and rough. In almost no other species of trees is there such a change from comparatively ungraceful youth to a superbly beautiful old age.

The second great type of American forest is deciduous. The trees have broad leaves quite unlike the slender needles or overlapping scales of

the northern evergreens. Each winter such forests
shed their leaves. Among the mountains where
the frosts come suddenly, the blaze of glory and
brilliance of color which herald the shedding of the
leaves are surpassed in no other part of the world.
Even the colors of the Painted Desert in northern
Arizona and the wonderful flowers of the California
plains are less pleasing. In the Painted Desert
the patches of red, yellow, gray-blue, white, pale
green, and black have a garish, almost repellent
appearance. In California the flame-colored acres
of poppies in some places, of white or yellow daisy-
like flowers in others, or of purple blossoms elsewhere have a softer expression than the bare
soil of the desert. Yet they lack the delicate blend-
ing and harmony of colors which is the greatest charm of the autumn foliage in the deciduous
forests. Even where the forests consist of such
trees as birches, beeches, aspens, or sycamores,
whose leaves merely turn yellow in the fall, the
contrast between this color and the green tint of
summer or the bare branches of winter adds a
spice of variety which is lacking in other and more
monotonous forests.

From still other points of view the deciduous
forest has an almost unequaled degree of variety.

7

In one place it consists of graceful little birches whose white trunks shimmering in the twilight form just the background for ghosts. Contrast them with the oak forest half a mile away. There the sense of gracefulness gives place to a feeling of strength. The lines are no longer vertical but horizontal. The knotted elbows of the branches recall the keels of sturdy merchantmen of bygone days. The acorns under foot suggest food for the herds of half-wild pigs which roam among the trees in many a southern county. Of quite another type are the stately forests of the Appalachians where splendid magnolia and tulip trees spread their broad limbs aloft at heights of one hundred feet or more.

Deciduous forests grow in the well-balanced regions where summer and winter approach equality, where neither is unduly long, and where neither is subject to prolonged drought. They extend southward from central New England, the Great Lakes, and Minnesota, to Mississippi, Arkansas, and eastern Texas. They predominate even in parts of such prairie States as Michigan, Indiana, southern Illinois, and southeastern Missouri. No part of the continent is more populous or more progressive than the regions once covered

by deciduous forests. In the United States nearly
sixty per cent of the inhabitants live in areas
reclaimed from such forests. Yet the area of the
forests is less than a quarter of the three million
square miles that make up the United States.

In their relation to human life the forests of
America differ far more than do either grass-lands
or deserts. In the far north, as we have seen, the
pine forests furnish one of the least favorable environments. In middle latitudes the deciduous
forests go to the opposite extreme and furnish the
most highly favored of the homes of man. Still
farther southward the increasing luxuriance of the
forests, especially along the Atlantic coast, renders
them less and less favorable to mankind. In
southern Mexico and Yucatan the stately equatorial rain forest, the most exuberant of all types
of vegetation and the most unconquerable by man,
makes its appearance. It forms a discontinuous
belt along the wet east coast and on the lower
slopes of the mountains from southern Yucatan to
Venezuela. Then it is interrupted by the grass-
lands of the Orinoco, but revives again in still
greater magnificence in the Guianas. Thence it
stretches not only along the coast but far into the
little known interior of the Great Amazon basin,

while southward it borders all the coast as far as southern Brazil. In the Amazon basin it reaches its highest development and becomes the crowning glory of the vegetable world, the most baffling obstacle to human progress.

Except in its evil effects on man, the equatorial rain forest is the antithesis of the forests of the extreme north. The equatorial trees are hardwood giants, broad leaved, bright flowered, and often fruit-bearing. The northern trees are softwood dwarfs, needle-leaved, flowerless, and cone-bearing. The equatorial trees are often branchless for one hundred feet, but spread at the top into a broad overarching canopy which shuts out the sun perpetually. The northern trees form sharp little pyramids with low, widely spreading branches at the base and only short twigs at the top. In the equatorial forests there is almost no underbrush. The animals, such as monkeys, snakes, parrots, and brilliant insects, live chiefly in the lofty tree-tops. In the northern forests there is almost nothing except underbrush, and the foxes, rabbits, weasels, ptarmigans, and mosquitoes live close to the ground in the shelter of the branches. Both forests are alike, however, in being practically un-inhabited by man. Each is peopled only by primi-

tive nomadic hunters who stand at the very bottom
in the scale of civilization.

Aside from the rain forest there are two other
types in tropical countries — jungle and scrub.
The distinction between rain forest, jungle, and
scrub is due to the amount and the season of
rainfall. An understanding of this distinction not
only explains many things in the present condition
of Latin America but also in the history of pre-
Columbian Central America. Forests, as we have
seen, require that the ground be moist throughout
practically the whole of the season that is warm
enough for growth. Since the warm season lasts
throughout the year within the tropics, dense
forests composed of uniformly large trees corresponding to our oaks, maples, and beeches will not
thrive unless the ground is wet most of the time.
Of course there may be no rain for a few weeks,
but there must be no long and regularly recurrent
periods of drought. Smaller trees and such species
as the cocoanut palm are much less exacting and
will flourish even if there is a dry period of several
months. Still smaller, bushy species will thrive
even when the rainfall lasts only two or three
months. Hence where the rainy season lasts most
of the year, rain forest prevails; where the rainy

and dry seasons do not differ greatly in length, tropical jungle is the dominant growth; and where the rainy season is short and the dry season long, the jungle degenerates into scrub or bush.

The relation of scrub, jungle, and rain forest is well illustrated in Yucatan, where the ancient Mayas reared their stately temples. On the northern coast the annual rainfall is only ten or fifteen inches and is concentrated largely in our summer months. There the country is covered with scrubby bushes six to ten feet high. These are beautifully green during the rainy season from June to October, but later in the year lose almost all their leaves. The landscape would be much like that of a thick, bushy pasture in the United States at the same season, were it not that in the late winter and early spring some of the bushes bear brilliant red, yellow, or white flowers. As one goes inland from the north coast of Yucatan the rainfall increases. The bushes become taller and denser, trees twenty feet high become numerous, and many rise thirty or forty feet or even higher. This is the jungle. Its smaller portions suggest a second growth of timber in the deciduous forests of the United States fifteen or twenty years after the cutting of the original forest, but here there

is much more evidence of rapid growth.   A few
species of bushes and trees may remain green
throughout the year, but during the dry season
most of the jungle plants lose their leaves, at least
in part.

With every mile that one advances into the more
rainy interior, the jungle becomes greener and
fresher, the density of the lower growths increases,
and the proportion of large trees becomes greater
until finally jungle gives place to genuine forest.
There many of the trees remain green throughout
the year.   They rise to heights of fifty or sixty feet
even on the borders of their province, and at the
top form a canopy so thick that the ground is shady
most of the time.   Even in the drier part of the
year when some of the leaves have fallen, the rays
of the sun scarcely reach the ground until nine or
ten o'clock in the morning.   Even at high noon
the sunlight straggles through only in small patches.
Long, sinuous lianas, often queerly braided, hang
down from the trees; epiphytes and various para-
sitic growths add their strange green and red to the
complex variety of vegetation.   Young palms grow
up almost in a day and block a trail which was
hewn out with much labor only a few months
before.   Wherever the death of old trees forms

an opening, a thousand seedlings begin a fierce race to reach the light. Everywhere the dominant note is intensely vigorous life, rapid growth, and quick decay.

In their effect on man, the three forms of tropical forest are very different. In the genuine rain forest agriculture is almost impossible. Not only does the poor native find himself baffled in the face of Nature, but the white man is equally at a loss. Many things combine to produce this result. Chief among them are malaria and other tropical diseases. When a few miles of railroad were being built through a strip of tropical forest along the coast of eastern Guatemala, it was impossible to keep the laborers more than twenty days at a time; indeed, unless they were sent away at the end of three weeks, they were almost sure to be stricken with virulent malarial fevers from which many died. An equally potent enemy of agriculture is the vegetation itself. Imagine the difficulty of cultivating a garden in a place where the weeds grow all the time and where many of them reach a height of ten or twenty feet in a single year. Perhaps there are people in the world who might culti-vate such a region and raise marvelous crops, but they are not the indolent people of tropical America; and it is in fact doubtful whether any kind of people could live permanently in the tropical forest and retain energy enough to carry on cultivation. Nowhere in the world is there such steady, damp heat as in these shadowy, windless depths far below the lofty tops of the rain forest. Nowhere is there greater disinclination to work than among the people who dwell in this region. Consequently in the vast rain forests of the Amazon basin and in similar small forests as far north as Central America, there are today practically no inhabitants except a mere handful of the poorest and most degraded people in the world. Yet in ancient times the northern border of the rain forest was the seat of America's most advanced civilization. The explanation of this contradiction will appear later.[1]

Tropical jungle borders the rain forest all the way from southern Mexico to southern Brazil. It treats man far better than does the rain forest. In marked contrast to its more stately neighbor, it contains abundant game. Wild fruits ripen at almost all seasons. A few banana plants and palm trees will well-nigh support a family. If corn is planted in a clearing, the return is large in proportion to the labor. So long as the population is not

[1] See pp. 169–171.

too dense, life is so easy that there is little to stimulate progress. Hence, although the people of the
jungle are fairly numerous, they have never played
much part in history. Far more important is the
rôle of those living in the tropical lands where
scrub is the prevailing growth. In our day, for
example, few tropical lowlands are more progressive than the narrow coastal strip of northern Yucatan. There on the border between jungle
and scrub the vegetation does not thrive sufficiently to make life easy for the chocolate-colored
natives. Effort is required if they would make a
living, yet the effort is not so great as to be beyond
the capacity of the indolent people of the tropics.

Leaving the forests, let us step out into the
broad, breezy grass-lands. One would scarcely expect that a journey poleward out of the forest of
northern Canada would lead to an improvement
in the conditions of human life, yet such is the case.
Where the growing season becomes so short that
even the hardiest trees disappear, grassy tundras
replace the forest. By furnishing food for such
animals as the musk-ox, they are a great help to
the handful of scattered Indians who dwell on the
northern edge of the forest. In summer, when the

animals grow fat on the short nutritious grass, the Indians follow them out into the open country and hunt them vigorously for food and skins to sustain life through the long dreary winter. In many cases the hunters would advance much farther into the grass-lands were it not that the abundant musk-oxen tempt the Eskimo of the seacoast also to leave their homes and both sides fear bloody encounters.

With the growth of civilization the advantage of the northern grass-lands over the northern forests becomes still more apparent. The domestic reindeer is beginning to replace the wild musk-ox. The reindeer people, like the Indian and Eskimo hunters, must be nomadic. Nevertheless their mode of life permits them to live in much greater numbers and on a much higher plane of civilization than the hunters. Since they hunt the fur-bearing animals in the neighboring forests during the winter, they diminish the food supply of the hunters who dwell permanently in the forest, and thus make their life still more difficult. The northern forests bid fair to decline in population rather than increase. In this New World of ours, strange as it may seem, the almost uninhabited forest regions of the far north and of the equator are probably more than twice as large as the desert areas with equally sparse population.

South of the tundras the grass-lands have a still greater advantage over the forests. In the forest region of the Laurentian highland abundant snow lasts far into the spring and keeps the ground so wet and cold that no crops can be raised. Moreover, because of the still greater abundance of snow in former times, the largest of ice sheets, as we have seen, accumulated there during the Glacial Period and scraped away most of the soil. The grassy plains, on the contrary, are favored not only by a deep, rich soil, much of which was laid down by the ice, but by the relative absence of snow in winter and the consequent rapidity with which the ground becomes warm in the spring. Hence the Canadian plains from the United States boundary northward to latitude 57° contain a prosperous agricultural population of over a million people, while the far larger forested areas in the same latitude support only a few thousand.

The question is often asked why, in a state of nature, trees are so scarce on the prairies — in Iowa, for instance — although they thrive when planted. In answer we are often told that up to the middle of the nineteenth century such vast herds of buffaloes roamed the prairies that seedling trees could never get a chance to grow. It is also said that prairie fires sweeping across the plains destroyed the little trees whenever they sprouted. Doubtless the buffaloes and the fires helped to prevent forest growth, but another factor appears to be still more important. All the States between the Mississippi River and the Rocky Mountains receive much more rain in summer than in winter. But as the soil is comparatively dry in the spring when the trees begin their growth, they are handicapped. They could grow if nothing else interfered with them, just as peas will grow in a garden if the weeds are kept out. If peas, however, are left uncared for, the weeds gain the upper hand and there are no peas the second year. If the weeds are left to contend with grass, the grass in the end prevails. In the eastern forest region, if the grass be left to itself, small trees soon spring up in its midst. In half a century a field of grass goes back to forest because trees are especially favored by the climate. In the same way in the prairies, grass is especially favored, for it is not weakened by the spring drought, and it grows abundantly until it forms the wonderful stretches of waving green where the buffalo once grew fat. Moreover the fine glacial soil of the prairies is so clayey and compact that the roots of trees cannot easily penetrate it. Since grasses send their roots only into the more friable upper layers of soil, they possess another great advantage over the trees.

Far to the south of the prairies lie the grass-lands of tropical America, of which the llanos of the Orinoco furnish a good example. Almost everywhere their plumed grasses have been left to grow undisturbed by the plough, and even grazing animals are scarce. These extremely flat plains are flooded for months in the rainy season from May to October and are parched in the dry season that follows. As trees cannot endure such extremes, grasses are the prevailing growth. Elsewhere the nature of the soil causes many other grassy tracts to be scattered among the tropical jungle and forest. Trees are at a disadvantage both in porous, sandy soils, where the water drains away too rapidly, and in clayey soil, where it is held so long that the ground is saturated for weeks or months at a time. South of the tropical portion of South America the vast pampas of Argentina closely resemble the North American prairies and the drier plains to the west of them. Grain in the east and cattle in the west are fast causing the disappearance of those great tussocks of tufted grasses eight or nine feet high which hold among grasses a position analogous to that of the Big Trees of California among trees of lower growth.

It is often said that America has no real deserts. This is true in the sense that there are no regions such as are found in Asia and Africa where one can travel a hundred miles at a stretch and scarcely see a sign of vegetation — nothing but barren gravel, graceful wavy sand dunes, hard wind-swept clay, or still harder rock salt broken into rough blocks with upturned edges. In the broader sense of the term, however, America has an abundance of deserts — regions which bear a thin cover of bushy vegetation but are too dry for agriculture without irrigation. On the north such deserts begin in southern Canada where a dry region abounding in small salt lakes lies at the eastern base of the Rocky Mountains. In the United States the deserts lie almost wholly between the Sierra Nevada and the Rocky Mountain ranges, which keep out any moisture that might come from either the west or the east. Beginning on the north with the sage-brush plateau of southern Washington, the desert expands to a width of seven hundred miles in the gray, sage-covered basins of Nevada and Utah. In southern California and Arizona the sage-brush gives place to smaller forms like the salt-bush, and the desert assumes a sterner aspect. Next comes the cactus desert extending from Arizona far south into Mexico. One of the notable features of the desert is the extreme heat of certain portions. Close to the Nevada border in southern California, Death Valley, 250 feet below sea-level, is the hottest place in America. There alone among the American regions familiar to the writer does one have that feeling of intense, overpowering aridity which prevails so often in the deserts of Arabia and Central Asia. Some years ago a Weather Bureau thermometer was installed in Death Valley at Furnace Creek, where the only flowing water in more than a hundred miles supports a depressing little ranch. There one or two white men, helped by a few Indians, raise alfalfa, which they sell at exorbitant prices to deluded prospectors searching for riches which they never find. Though the terrible heat ruins the health of the white men in a year or two, so that they have to move away, they have succeeded in keeping a thermometer record for some years. No other properly exposed, out-of-door thermometer in the United States, or perhaps

in the world, is so familiar with a temperature of
100° F. or more. During the period of not quite
fifteen hundred days from the spring of 1911 to
May, 1915, a maximum temperature of 100° F.
or more was reached on five hundred and forty-
eight days, or more than one-third of the time. On
July 10, 1913, the mercury rose to 134° F. and
touched the top of the tube. How much higher it
might have gone no one can tell. That day marks
the limit of temperature yet reached in this country according to official records. In the summer of
1914 there was one night when the thermometer
dropped only to 114° F., having been 128° F. at
noon. The branches of a pepper-tree whose roots
had been freshly watered wilted as a flower wilts
when broken from the stalk.

East and south of Death Valley lies the most
interesting section of the American desert, the so-
called succulent desert of southern Arizona and
northern Mexico. There in greatest profusion
grow the cacti, perhaps the latest and most highly
specialized of all the great families of plants.
There occur such strange scenes as the "forests"
of suhuaros, whose giant columns have already
been described. Their beautiful crowns of large
white flowers produce a fruit which is one of the

8

mainstays of the Papagos and other Indians of the regions. In this same region the yucca is highly developed, and its tall stalks of white or greenish flowers make the desert appear like a flower garden. In fact this whole desert, thanks to light rains in summer as well as winter, appears extraordinarily green and prosperous. Its fair appearance has deceived many a poor settler who has vainly tried to cultivate it.

Farther south the deserts of America are largely confined to plateaus like those of Mexico and Peru or to basins sheltered on all sides from rain-bearing winds. In such basins the suddenness of the transition from one type of vegetation to another is astonishing. In Guatemala, for instance, the coast is bordered by thick jungle which quickly gives place to magnificent rain forest a few miles inland. This continues two or three score miles from the coast until a point is reached where mountains begin to obstruct the rain-bearing trade-winds. At once the rain forest gives place to jungle; in a few miles jungle in its turn is replaced by scrub; and shortly the scrub degenerates to mere desert bush. Then in another fifty miles one rises to the main plateau passing once more through scrub. This time the scrub gives place to grass-lands

diversified by deciduous trees and pines which give
the country a distinctly temperate aspect. On
such plateaus the chief civilization of the tropical
Latin-American countries now centers. In the
past, however, the plateaus were far surpassed by
the Maya lowlands of Yucatan and Guatemala.

We are wont to think of deserts as places where
the plants are of few kinds and not much crowded.
As a matter of fact, an ordinary desert supports a
much greater variety of plants than does either a
forest or a prairie. The reason is simple. Every
desert contains wet spots near springs or in swamps.
Such places abound with all sorts of water-loving
plants. The deserts also contain a few valleys
where the larger streams keep the ground moist
at all seasons. In such places the variety of trees
is as great as in many forests. Moreover almost all
deserts have short periods of abundant moisture.
At such times the seeds of all sorts of little annual
plants, including grasses, daisies, lupines, and a
host of others, sprout quickly, and give rise to a
carpet of vegetation as varied and beautiful as
that of the prairie. Thus the desert has not only
its own peculiar bushes and succulents but many of
the products of vegetation in swamps, grass-lands,
and forests.

Though much of the ground is bare in the desert, the plants are actually crowded together as closely as possible. The showers of such regions are usually so brief that they merely wet the surface. At a depth of a foot or more the soil of many deserts never becomes moist from year's end to year's end. It is useless for plants to send their roots deep down under such circumstances, for they might not reach water for a hundred feet. Their only recourse is to spread horizontally. The farther they spread, the more water they can absorb after the scanty showers. Hence the plants of the desert throttle one another by extending their roots horizontally, just as those of the forest kill one another by springing rapidly upward and shutting out the light.

Vegetation, whether in forests, grass-lands, or deserts, is the primary source of human sustenance. Without it man would perish miserably; and where it is deficient, he cannot rise to great heights in the scale of civilization. Yet strangely enough the scantiness of the vegetation of the deserts was a great help in the ascent of man. Only in dry regions could primitive man compete with nature in fostering the right kind of vegetation. In such regions arose the nations which first practised agriculture. There man became comparatively civilized while his contemporaries were still nomadic hunters in the grass-lands and the forests.

CHAPTER V

THE RED MAN IN AMERICA

WHEN the white man first explored America, the parts of the continent that had made most progress were by no means those that are most advanced today.[1] None of the inhabitants, to be sure, had risen above barbarism. Yet certain nations or tribes had advanced much higher than others. There was a great contrast, for example, between the well-organized barbarians of Peru and the almost completely unorganized Athapascan savages near Hudson Bay.

In the northern continent aboriginal America reached its highest development in three typical

[1] In the present chapter most of the facts as to the Indians north of Mexico are taken from the admirable *Handbook of American Indians North of Mexico*, edited by F. W. Hodge, Smithsonian Institution, Bureau of Ethnology, Bulletin 30, Washington, 1907, two volumes. In summing up the character and achievements of the Indians I have drawn also on other sources, but have everywhere taken pains to make no statements which are not abundantly supported by this authoritative publication. In some cases I have not hesitated to paraphrase considerable portions of its articles.

Gravure, Andersen–Lamb Co. N.Y.

environments. The first of these regions centered in the valley of Mexico where dwelt the Aztecs, but it extended as far north as the Pueblos in Arizona and New Mexico. The special feature of the environment was the relatively dry, warm climate with the chief rainfall in summer. The Indians living in this environment were notable for their comparatively high social organization and for religious ceremonials whose elaborateness has rarely been surpassed. On the whole, the people of this summer rain or Mexican type were not warlike and offered little resistance to European conquest. Some tribes, to be sure, fought fiercely at first, but yielded within a few years; the rest submitted to the lordly Spaniards almost without a murmur. Their civilization, if such we may call it, had long ago seen its best days. The period of energy and progress had passed, and a time of inertia and decay had set in.

A century after the Spaniards had overcome the aborigines of Mexico, other Europeans — French, English, and Dutch — came into contact with a sturdier type of red man, best represented by the Iroquois or Five Nations of central New York. This more active type dwelt in a physical environment notable for two features — the abundance of

cyclonic storms bringing rain or snow at all seasons
and the deciduous forest which thickly covered
the whole region. Unlike the Mexican, the civilization of the Iroquois was young, vigorous, and
growing. It had not learned to express itself in
durable architectural forms like those of Mexico,
nor could it rival the older type in social and
religious organization. In political organization,
however, the Five Nations had surpassed the other
aboriginal peoples of North America. When the
white man became acquainted with the Iroquois
in the seventeenth century, he found five of their
tribes organized into a remarkable confederation
whose avowed object was to abolish war among
themselves and to secure to all the members the
peaceful exercise of their rights and privileges.
So well was the confederation organized that, in
spite of war with its enemies, it persisted for at
least two hundred years.

One of the chief characteristics of the Iroquois
was their tremendous energy. They were so energetic that they pursued their enemies with an
implacable relentlessness similar to the restless
eagerness with which the people of the region from
New York to Chicago now pursue their business
enterprises. This led the Iroquois to torture their

prisoners with the utmost ingenuity and cruelty.
Not only did the savages burn and mutilate their
captives, but they sometimes added the last re-
finement of torture by compelling the suffering
wretches to eat pieces of flesh cut from their own
bodies. Energy may lead to high civilization, but
it may also lead to excesses of evil.

The third prominent aboriginal type was that
of the fishermen of the coast of British Columbia, especially the Haidas of the Queen Charlotte
Islands. The most important features of their
environment were the submerged coast with its
easy navigation, the mild oceanic climate, and the
dense pine forests. The Haidas, like the Iroquois,
appear to have been a people who were still advancing. Such as it was, their greatness was apparently the product of their own ingenuity and
not, like that of the Mexicans, an inheritance from
a greater past. The Haidas lacked the relentless
energy of the Iroquois and shared the comparatively gentle character which prevailed among all
the Indians along the Pacific Coast. They were by
no means weaklings, however. Commercially, for
instance, they seem to have been more advanced
than any North American tribe except those in the
Mexican area. In architecture they stood equally

high. We are prone to think of the Mexicans as the best architects among the aborigines, but when the white man came even the Aztecs were merely imitating the work of their predecessors. The Haidas, on the contrary, were showing real originality. They had no stone with which to build, for their country is so densely forested that stone is rarely visible. They were remarkably skillful, however, in hewing great beams from the forest. With these they constructed houses whose carved totem poles and graceful façades gave promise of an architecture of great beauty. Taking into account the difficulties presented by a material which was not durable and by tools which were nothing but bits of stone, we must regard their totem poles and mural decorations as real contributions to primitive architecture.

In addition to these three highest types of the red man there were many others. Each, as we shall see, owed its peculiarities largely to the physical surroundings in which it lived. Of course different tribes possessed different degrees of innate ability, but the chief differences in their habits and mode of life arose from the topography, the climate, the plants, and the animals which formed the geographical setting of their homes.

In previous chapters we have gained some idea
of the topography of the New World and of the
climate in its relation to plants and animals. We
have also seen that climate has much to do with
human energy. We have not, however, gained a
sufficiently clear idea of the distribution of climatic
energy.   A map of the world showing how energy
would be distributed if it depended entirely upon
climate clarifies the subject. The dark shading of
the map indicates those regions where energy is
highest.   It is based upon measurements of the
strength of scores of individuals, upon the scholas-
tic records of hundreds of college students, upon
the piecework of thousands of factory operatives,
and upon millions of deaths and births in a score of
different countries.   It takes account of three chief
climatic conditions — temperature, humidity, and
variability.   It also takes account of mental as well
as physical ability.   Underneath it is a map of the
distribution of civilization on the basis of the
opinion of fifty authorities in fifteen different countries.   The similarity of the two maps is so striking
that there can be little question that today the
distribution of civilization agrees closely with the
distribution of climatic energy.   When Egypt,
Babylonia, Greece, and Rome were at the height of

their power this agreement was presumably the same, for the storm belt which now gives variability and hence energy to the thickly shaded regions in our two maps then apparently lay farther south.

It is generally considered that no race has been more closely dependent upon physical environment than were the Indians. Why, then, did the energizing effect of climate apparently have less effect upon them than upon the other great races? Why were not the most advanced Indian tribes found in the same places where white civilization is today most advanced? Climatic changes might in part account for the difference, but, although such changes apparently took place on a large scale in earlier times, there is no evidence of anything except minor fluctuations since the days of the first white settlements. Racial inheritance likewise may account for some of the differences among the various tribes, but it was probably not the chief factor. That factor was apparently the condition of agriculture among people who had neither iron tools nor beasts of burden. Civilization has never made much progress except when there has been a permanent cultivation of the ground. It has been said that "the history of agriculture is the history of man in his most primitive and most permanent aspect." If we examine the achievements and manner of life of the Indians in relation to the effect of climate upon agriculture and human energy, as well as in relation to the more obvious features of topography and vegetation, we shall understand why the people of aboriginal America in one part of the continent differed so greatly from those in another part.

In the far north the state of the inhabitants today is scarcely different from what it was in the days of Columbus. Then, as now, the Eskimos had practically no political or social organization beyond the family or the little group of relatives who lived in a single camp. They had no permanent villages, but moved from place to place according to the season in search of fish, game, and birds. They lived this simple life not because they lacked ability but because of their surroundings. Their kayaks or canoes are marvels of ingenuity. With no materials except bones, driftwood, and skins they made boats which fulfilled their purpose with extraordinary perfection. Seated in the small, round hole which is the only opening in the deck of his canoe, the Eskimo hunter ties his skin jacket tightly outside the circular gunwale and is thus shut into a practically water-tight compartment.

Though the waves dash over him, scarcely a drop enters the craft as he skims along with his double paddle among cakes of floating ice. So, too, the snowhouse with its anterooms and curved entrance passage is as clever an adaptation to the needs of wanderers in a land of ice and snow as is the skyscraper to the needs of a busy commercial people crowded into great cities. The fact that the oil-burning, soapstone lamps of the Eskimo were the only means of producing artificial light in aboriginal America, except by ordinary fires, is another tribute to the ingenuity of these northerners. So, too, is the fire-drill by which they alone devised a means of increasing the speed with which one stick could be twirled against another to produce fire. In view of these clever inventions it seems safe to say that the Eskimo has remained a no-madic savage not because he lacks inventive skill but partly because the climate deadens his energies and still more because it forbids him to practice agriculture.

Southward and inland from the coastal homes of the Eskimo lies the great region of the northern pine forests. It extends from the interior of Alaska southeastward in such a way as to include most of the Canadian Rockies, the northern plains from

Great Bear Lake almost to Lake Winnipeg, and most of the great Laurentian shield around Hudson Bay and in the peninsula of Labrador. Except among the inhabitants of the narrow Pacific slope and those of the shores of Labrador and the St. Lawrence Valley, a single type of barbarism prevailed among the Indians of all the vast pine forest area. Only in a small section of the wheat-raising plains of Alberta and Saskatchewan have their habits greatly changed because of the arrival of the white man. Now as always the Indians in these northern regions are held back by the long, benumbing winters. They cannot practice agriculture, for no crops will grow. They cannot depend to any great extent upon natural vegetation, for aside from blueberries, a few lichens, and one or two other equally insignificant products, the forests furnish no food except animals. These lowly people seem to have been so occupied with the severe struggle with the elements that they could not even advance out of savagery into barbarism. They were homeless nomads whose movements were determined largely by the food supply.

Among the Athapascans who occupied all the western part of the northern pine forests, clothing was made of deerskins with the hair left on. The lodges were likewise of deer or caribou skins, although farther south these were sometimes replaced by bark. The food of these tribes consisted of caribou, deer, moose, and musk-ox together with smaller animals such as the beaver and hare. They also ate various kinds of birds and the fish found in the numerous lakes and rivers. They killed deer by driving them into an angle formed by two converging rows of stakes, where they were shot by hunters lying in wait. Among the Kawchodinne tribe near Great Bear Lake hares were the chief source of both food and clothing. When an unusually severe winter or some other disaster diminished the supply, the Indians believed that the animals had mounted to the sky by means of the trees and would return by the same way. In 1841 owing to scarcity of hares many of this tribe died of starvation, and numerous acts of cannibalism are said to have occurred. Small wonder that civilization was low and that infanticide, especially of female children, was common. Among such people women were naturally treated with a minimum of respect. Since they were not skilled as hunters, there was relatively little which they could contribute toward the sustenance of the family. Hence they were held in low esteem, for

among most primitive people woman is valued
largely in proportion to her economic contribution.
Her low position is illustrated by the peculiar
funeral custom of the Takulli, an Athapascan tribe
on the Upper Frazer River. A widow was obliged
to remain upon the funeral pyre of her husband till
the flames reached her own body. When the fire
had died down she collected the ashes of her dead
and placed them in a basket, which she was obliged
to carry with her during three years of servitude in
the family of her husband. At the end of that
time a feast was held, when she was released from
thraldom and permitted to remarry if she desired.

Poor and degraded as the people of the northern
forests may have been, they had their good traits.
The Kutchins of the Yukon and Lower Mackenzie
regions, though they killed their female children,
were exceedingly hospitable and kept guests for
months. Each head of a family took his turn in
feasting the whole band. On such occasions eti-
quette required the host to fast until the guests
had departed. At such feasts an interesting wres-
tling game was played. First the smallest boys
began to wrestle. The victors wrestled with those
next in strength and so on until finally the strongest
and freshest man in the band remained the final

9

victor. Then the girls and women went through the same progressive contest. It is hard to determine whether the people of the northern pine forest were more or less competent than their Eskimo neighbors. It perhaps makes little difference, for it is doubtful whether even a race with brilliant natural endowments could rise far in the scale of civilization under conditions so highly adverse.

The Eskimos of the northern coasts and the people of the pine forests were not the only aborigines whose development was greatly retarded because they could not practice agriculture. All the people of the Pacific coast from Alaska to Lower California were in similar circumstances. Nevertheless those living along the northern part of this coast rose to a much higher level than did those of California. This has sometimes been supposed to show that geographical environment has little influence upon civilization, but in reality it proves exactly the opposite.

The coast of British Columbia was one of the three chief centers of aboriginal America. As *The Encyclopædia Britannica*[1] puts it: "The Haida people constituted with little doubt the finest race

[1] 11th Edition, vol. XXII, p. 730.

and that most advanced in the arts of the entire west coast of North America." They and their almost equally advanced Tlingit and Tsimshian neighbors on the mainland displayed much mechanical skill, especially in canoe-building, woodcarving, and the working of stone and copper, as well as in making blankets and baskets. To this day they earn a considerable amount of money by selling their carved objects of wood and slate to traders and tourists. Their canoes were hollowed out of logs of cedar and were often very large. Houses which were sometimes 40 by 100 feet were built of huge cedar beams and planks, which were first worked with stone and were then put together at great feasts. These correspond to the "raising bees" at which the neighbors gathered to erect the frames of houses in early New England. Each Haida house ordinarily had a single carved totem pole in the middle of the gable end which faced toward the beach. Often the end posts in front were also carved and the whole house was painted. Another evidence of the fairly advanced state of the Haidas was their active commercial intercourse with regions hundreds of miles away. At their "potlatches," as the raising bees were called by the whites, traffic went on vigorously.

Carved copper plates were among the articles which they esteemed of highest value. Standing in the tribe depended on the possession of property rather than on ability in war, in which respect the Haidas were more like the people of today than were any of the other Indian tribes.

Slavery was common among the Haidas. Even as late as 1861, 7800 Tlingits held 828 slaves. Slavery may not be a good institution in itself, but it indicates that people are well-to-do, that they dwell in permanent abodes, and that they have a well-established social order. Among the more backward Iroquois, captives rarely became genuine slaves, for the social and economic organization was not sufficiently developed to admit of this. The few captives who were retained after a fight were adopted into the tribe of the captors or else were allowed to live with them and shift for themselves — a practice very different from that of the Haidas.

Another feature of the Haidas' life which showed comparative progress was the social distinctions which existed among them. One of the ways in which individuals maintained their social position was by giving away quantities of goods of all kinds at the potlatches which they organized. A man

sometimes went so far as to strip himself of nearly every possession except his house. In return for this, however, he obtained what seemed to him an abundant reward in the respect with which his fellow-tribesmen afterward regarded him. At subsequent potlatches he received in his turn a measure of their goods in proportion to his own gifts, so that he was sometimes richer than before. These potlatches were social as well as industrial functions, and dancing and singing were interspersed with the feasting. One of the amusements was a musical contest in which singers from one tribe or band would contend with one another as to which could remember the greatest number of songs or accurately repeat a new song after hearing it for the first time. At the potlatches the children of chiefs were initiated into secret societies. They had their noses, ears, and lips pierced for ornaments, and some of them were tattooed. This great respect for social position which the Haidas manifested is doubtless far from ideal, but it at least indicates that a part of the tribe was sufficiently advanced to accumulate property and to pass it on to its descendants — a custom that is almost impossible among tribes which move from place to place.

The question suggests itself why these coast barbarians were so much in advance of their neighbors a few hundred miles away in the pine woods of the mountains. The climate was probably one reason for this superiority. Instead of being in a region like the center of the pine forests of British Columbia where human energy is sapped by six or eight months of winter, the Haidas enjoyed conditions like those of Scotland. Although snow fell occasionally, severe cold was unknown. Nor was there great heat in summer. The Haidas dwelt where both bodily strength and mental activity were stimulated. In addition to this advantage of a favorable climate these Indians had a large and steady supply of food close at hand. Most of their sustenance was obtained from the sea and from the rivers, in which the runs of salmon furnished abundant provisions, which rarely failed. In Hecate Strait, between the Queen Charlotte Islands and the mainland, there were wonderfully productive halibut fisheries, from which a supply of fish was dried and packed away for the winter, so that there was always a store of provisions on hand. The forests in their turn furnished berries and seeds, as well as bears, mountain goats, and other game.

Moreover the people of the northwest coast had the advantage of not being forced to move from place to place in order to follow the fish. They lived on a drowned shore where bays, straits, and sounds are extraordinarily numerous. The great waves of the Pacific are shut out by the islands so that the waterways are almost always safe for canoes. Instead of moving their dwellings in order to follow the food supply, as the Eskimo and the people of the pine forest were forced to do, the Haidas and their neighbors were able without difficulty to bring their food home. At all seasons the canoes made it easy to transport large supplies of fish from places even a hundred miles away. Having settled dwellings, the Haidas could accumulate property and acquire that feeling of permanence which is one of the most important conditions for the development of civilization. Doubtless the Haidas were intellectually superior to many other tribes, but even if they had not been greatly superior, their surroundings would probably have made them stand relatively high in the scale of civilization.

Southward from the Haidas, around Puget Sound and in Washington and Oregon, there was a gradual decline in civilization. The Chinook

Indians of the lower Columbia, beyond the limits of the great northern archipelago, had large communal houses occupied by three or four families of twenty or more individuals. Their villages were thus fairly permanent, although there was much moving about in summer owing to the nature of the food supply, which consisted chiefly of salmon, with roots and berries indigenous to the region. The people were noted as traders not only among themselves but with surrounding tribes. They were extremely skillful in handling their canoes, which were well made, hollowed out of single logs, and often of great size. In disposition they are described as treacherous and deceitful, especially when their cupidity was aroused. Slaves were common and were usually obtained by barter from surrounding tribes, though occasionally by successful raids. These Indians of Oregon by no means rivaled the Haidas, for their food supply was less certain and they did not have the advantage of easy water communication, which did so much to raise the Haidas to a high level of development.

Of the tribes farther south an observer says: "In general rudeness of culture the California Indians are scarcely above the Eskimo, and whereas the lack of development of the Eskimo on many sides of their nature is reasonably attributable in part to their difficult and limiting environment, the Indians of California inhabit a country naturally as favorable, it would seem, as it might be. If the degree of civilization attained by a people depends in any large measure on their habitat, as does not seem likely, it might be concluded from the case of the California Indians that natural advantages were an impediment rather than an incentive to progress." In some of the tribes, such as the Hupa, for example, there existed no organization and no formalities in the government of the village. Formal councils were unknown, although the chief might and often did ask advice of his men in a collected body. In general the social structure of the California Indians was so simple and loose that it is hardly correct to speak of their tribes. Whatever solidarity there was among these people was due in part to family ties and in part to the fact that they lived in the same village and spoke the same dialect. Between different groups of these Indians, the common bond was similarity of language as well as frequency and cordiality of intercourse. In so primitive a condition of society there was neither necessity nor opportunity for differences of rank. The influence of chiefs was small and no distinct classes of slaves were known.

Extreme poverty was the chief cause of the low social and political organization of these Indians. The Maidus in the Sacramento Valley were so poor that, in addition to consuming every possible vegetable product, they not only devoured all birds except the buzzard, but ate badgers, skunks, wildcats, and mountain lions, and even consumed salmon bones and deer vertebræ. They gathered grasshoppers and locusts by digging large shallow pits in a meadow or flat. Then, setting fire to the grass on all sides, they drove the insects into the pit. Their wings being burned off by the flames, the grasshoppers were helpless and were thus collected by the bushel. Again of the Moquelumne, one of the largest tribes in central California, it is said that their houses were simply frameworks of poles and brush which in winter were covered with earth. In summer they erected cone-shaped lodges of poles among the mountains. In favorable years they gathered large quantities of acorns, which formed their principal food, and stored them for winter use in granaries raised above the ground. Often, however, the crop was poor, and the Indians were left on the verge of starvation.

Finally in the far south, in the peninsula of Lower California, the tribes were "probably the lowest in culture of any Indians in North America, for their inhospitable environment which made them wanderers, was unfavorable to the foundation of government even of the rude and unstable kind found elsewhere." The Yuman tribes of the mountains east of Santiago wore sandals of maguey fiber and descended from their own territory among the mountains "to eat calabash and other fruits" that grew beside the Colorado River. They were described as "very dirty on account of the much mescal they eat." Others speak of them as "very filthy in their habits. To overcome vermin they coat their heads with mud with which they also paint their bodies. On a hot day it is by no means unusual to see them wallowing in the mud like pigs." They were "exceedingly poor, having no animals except foxes of which they had a few skins. The dress of the women in summer was a shirt and a bark skirt. The men appear to have been practically unclothed during this season. The practice of selling children seems to have been common. Their sustenance was fish, fruits, vegetables, and seeds of grass, and many of the tribes were said to have been dreadfully scorbutic."

A little to the east of these degraded savages the much more advanced Mohave tribe had its home on the lower Colorado River. The contrast between these neighboring tribes throws much light on the reason for the low estate of the California Indians. "No better example of the power of environment to better man's condition can be found than that shown as the lower Colorado is reached. Here are tribes of the same family (as those of Lower California) remarkable not only for their fine physical development, but living in settled villages with well-defined tribal lines, practising a rude, but effective, agriculture, and well advanced in many primitive Indian arts. The usual Indian staples were raised except tobacco, these tribes preferring a wild tobacco of their region to the cultivated."[1]

This quotation is highly significant. With it should be compared the fact that there is no evidence that corn or anything else was cultivated in California west of the Rio Colorado Valley. California is a region famous throughout America for its agriculture, but its crops are European in origin. Even in the case of fruits, such as the grape, which have American counterparts, the varieties actually

[1] Hodge, *Handbook of American Indians.*

cultivated were brought from Europe. Wheat and barley, the chief foodstuffs for which California and similar subtropical regions are noted, were unknown in the New World before the coming of the white man. In pre-Columbian America corn was the only cultivated cereal. The other great staples of early American agriculture were beans and pumpkins. All three are preëminently summer crops and need much water in July and August. In California there is no rain at this season. Though the fall rains, which begin to be abundant in October and November, do not aid these summer crops, they favor wheat and barley. The winter rains and the comparatively warm winter weather permit these grains to grow slowly but continuously. When the warm spring arrives, there is still enough rain to permit wheat and barley to make a rapid growth and to mature their seeds long before the long, dry summer begins. The comparatively dry weather of May and June is just what these cereals need to ripen the crop, but it is fatal to any kind of agriculture which depends on summer rain.

Crops can of course be grown during the summer in California by means of irrigation, but this is rarely a simple process. If irrigation is to be

effective in California, it cannot depend on the
small streams which practically dry up during the
long, rainless summer, but it must depend on
comparatively large streams which flow in well-
defined channels. With our modern knowledge
and machinery it is easy for us to make canals and
ditches and to prepare the level fields needed to
utilize this water. A people with no knowledge of
agriculture, however, and with no iron tools cannot suddenly begin to practice a complex and
highly developed system of agriculture. In California there is little or none of the natural summer
irrigation which, in certain parts of America,
appears to have been the most important factor
leading to the first steps in tilling the ground.
The lower Colorado, however, floods broad areas
every summer. Here, as on the Nile, the retiring
floods leave the land so moist that crops can easily
be raised. Hence the Mohave Indians were able
to practice agriculture and to rise well above their
kinsmen not only in Lower California but throughout the whole State.

In the Rocky Mountain region of the United
States, just as on the Pacific coast, the condition of the tribes deteriorated more and more the
farther they lived to the south. In the regions where

the rainfall comes in summer, however, and hence
favors primitive agriculture, there was a marked
improvement. The Kutenai tribes lived near the
corner where Idaho, Montana, and British Columbia now meet. They appear to have been of
rather high grade, noteworthy for their morality,
kindness, and hospitality. More than any other
Indians of the Rocky Mountain region, they
avoided drunkenness and lewd intercourse with the
whites. Their mental ability was comparatively
high, as appears from their skill in buffalo-hunting,
in making dugouts and bark canoes, and in con-
structing sweat-houses and lodges of both skins
and rushes. Even today the lower Kutenai are
noted for their water-tight baskets of split roots.
Moreover the degree to which they used the plants
that grew about them for food, medicine, and eco-
nomical purposes was noteworthy. They also had
an esthetic appreciation of several plants and
flowers — a gift rare among Indians. These people
lived in the zone of most stimulating climate and,
although they did not practice agriculture and had
little else in their surroundings to help them to rise
above the common level, they dwelt in a region
where there was rain enough in summer to prevent their being on the verge of starvation, as

the Indians of California usually were. Moreover they were near enough to the haunts of the buffalo to depend on that great beast for food. Since one buffalo supplies as much food as a hundred rabbits, these Indians were vastly better off than the people of the drier parts of the western coast.

South of the home of the Kutenai, in eastern Oregon, southern Idaho, Nevada, Utah, and neighboring regions dwelt the Utes and other Shoshoni tribes. In this region the rainfall, which is no greater than that of California, occurs chiefly in winter. The long summer is so dry that, except by highly developed methods of irrigation, agriculture is impossible. Hence it is not surprising to find a traveler in 1850 describing one tribe of the Ute family as "without exception the most miserable looking set of human beings I ever saw. They have hitherto subsisted principally on snakes, lizards, roots." The lowest of all the Ute tribes were those who lived in the sage-brush. The early explorer, Bonneville, found the tribes of Snake River wintering in brush shelters without roofs — merely heaps of brush piled high, behind which the Indians crouched for protection from wind and snow. Crude as such shelters may seem, they were the best that could be constructed by people who dwelt where there was no vegetation except little bushes, and where the soil was for the most part sandy or so salty that it could not easily be made into adobe bricks.

The food of these Utes and Shoshonis was no better than their shelters. There were no large animals for them to hunt; rabbits were the best that they could find. Farther to the east, where the buffalo wandered during part of the year and where there are some forests, the food was better, the shelters were more effective, and, in general, the standard of living was higher, although racially the two groups of people were alike. In this case, as in others, the people whose condition was lowest were apparently as competent as those whose material conditions were much better. Today, although the Ute Indians, like most of their race, are rather slow, some tribes, such as the Payutes, are described as not only "peaceful and moral," but also "industrious." They are highly commended for their good qualities by those who have had the best opportunities for judging. While not as bright in intellect as some of the prairie tribes whom we shall soon consider, they appear to possess more solidity of character. By their

10

willingness and efficiency as workers they have made themselves necessary to the white farmers and have thus supplied themselves with good clothing and many of the comforts of life. They have resisted, too, many of the evils coming from the advance of civilization, so that one agent speaks of these Indians as presenting the singular anomaly of improving by contact with the whites. Apparently their extremely low condition in former times was due merely to that same handicap of environment which kept back the Indians of California.

Compare these backward but not wholly ungifted Utes with the Hopi who belonged to the same stock. The relatively high social organization of the latter people and the intricacy and significance of their religious ceremonials are well known. Mentally the Hopi seem to be the equal of any tribe, but it is doubtful whether they have much more innate capacity than many of their more backward neighbors. Nevertheless they made much more progress before the days of the white man, as can easily be seen in their artistic development. Every one who has crossed the continent by the Santa Fé route knows how interesting and beautiful are their pottery, basketry, and weaving. Not only in art but also in government the Hopi are highly advanced. Their governing body is a council of hereditary elders together with the chiefs of religious fraternities. Among these officials there is a speaker chief and a war chief, but there seems never to have been any supreme chief of all the Hopi. Each pueblo has an hereditary chief who directs all the communal work, such as the cleaning of the springs and the general care of the village. Crimes are rare. This at first sight seems strange in view of the fact that no penalty was inflicted for any crime except sorcery, but under Hopi law all transgressions could be reduced to sorcery. One of the most striking features of Hopi life was its rich religious development. The Hopi recognized a large number of supernatural beings and had a great store of most interesting and poetic mythological tales. The home of the Hopi would seem at first sight as unfavorable to progress as that of their Ute cousins, but the Hopi have the advantage of being the most northwesterly representatives of the Indians who dwell within the regions of summer rain. Fortunately for them, their country is too desert and unforested for them to subsist to any great degree by the chase. They are thus forced to devote all their energy to agriculture, through which they have developed a relatively high standard of living. They dwell far enough south to have their heaviest rainfall in summer and not in winter, as is the case in Utah, so that they are able to cultivate crops of corn and beans. Where such an intensive system of agriculture prevails, the work of women is as valuable as that of men. The position of woman is thus relatively high among the Hopi, for she is useful not only for her assistance in the labors of the field but also for her skill in preserving the crops, grinding the flour, and otherwise preparing the comparatively varied food which this tribe fortunately possesses.

From northern New Mexico and Arizona to Mexico City summer rains, dry winters, and still drier springs, are the rule. Forests are few, and much of the country is desert. The more abundant the rains, the greater the number of people and the greater the opportunities for the accumulation of wealth, and thus for that leisure which is necessary to part of a community if civilization is to make progress. That is one reason why the civilization of the summer rain people becomes more highly developed as they go from north to south. The fact that the altitude of the country increases from the United States border southward also tends in the same direction, for it causes the climate to be cooler and more bracing at Mexico City than at places farther north.

The importance of summer rains in stimulating growth and in facilitating the early stages of agriculture is noteworthy. Every one familiar with Arizona and New Mexico knows how the sudden summer showers fill the mountain valleys with floods which flow down upon the plain and rapidly spread out into broad, thin sheets, often known as *playas*. There the water stands a short time and then either sinks into the ground or evaporates. Such places are favored with the best kind of natural irrigation, and after the first shower it is an easy matter for the primitive farmer to go out and drop grains of corn into holes punched with a stick. Thereafter he can count on other showers to water his field while the corn sprouts and grows to maturity. All that he needs to do is to watch the field to protect it from the rare depredations of wild animals. As time goes on the primitive farmer realizes the advantage of leading the water to particularly favorable spots and thus begins to develop a system of artificial irrigation. In regions where such advantageous conditions prevail, the people who live permanently in one place succeed best, for the work that they do one year helps them the next. They are not greatly troubled by weeds, for, though grasses grow as well as corn in the places where the water spreads out, the grasses take the form of little clumps which can easily be pulled up. In the drier parts of the area of summer rain, it becomes necessary to conserve the water supply to the utmost. The Hopi consider sandy fields the best, for the loose sand on top acts as a natural blanket to prevent evaporation from the underlying layers. Sometimes in dry seasons the Hopi use extraordinary methods to help their seeds to sprout. For instance, they place a seed in a ball of saturated mud which they bury beneath several inches of sand. As the sand prevents evaporation, practically all the water is retained for the use of the seed, which thereupon sprouts and grows some inches by the time the first summer floods arrive.

The Indians of the Great Plains lived a very different life from that of the natives of either the mountains or the Pacific coast. In the far north, to be sure, the rigorous climate caused all the Indians to live practically alike, whether in the Rockies, the plains, or the Laurentian highland.

South of them, in that great central expanse
stretching from the latitude of Lake Winnipeg to
the Rio Grande River, the Indians of the plains
possessed a relatively uniform type of life peculiar
to themselves. This individuality was due partly
to the luxuriant carpet of grass which covered the
plains and partly to the supply of animal food af-
forded by the vast herds of buffaloes which roamed
in tens of thousands throughout the whole territory. The grass was important chiefly because it
prevented the Indians from engaging in agriculture,
for it must never be forgotten that the Indians had
neither iron tools nor beasts of burden to aid them
in overcoming the natural difficulties in the way
of agriculture. To be sure, they did occasionally
pound meteoric iron into useful implements, but
this substance was so rare that probably not one
Indian in a hundred had ever seen a piece. The
Indians were quite familiar with copper, but there
is not the slightest evidence that they had discovered any means of hardening it. Metals played
no real part in the life of any of the Indians of
America, and without such tools as iron spades and
hoes it was impossible for them to cultivate grass-
land. If they burned the prairie and dropped seeds
into holes, the corn or beans which they thus

planted were sure to be choked by the quickly springing grass. To dig away the tough sod around the hole for each seed would require an almost incredible amount of work even with iron tools. To accomplish this with wooden spades, rude hoes made of large flakes of flint, or the shoulder blades of the buffalo, was impossible on any large scale. Now and then in some river bottom where the grass grew in clumps and could be easily pulled up, a little agriculture was possible. That is all that seems to have been attempted on the great grassy plains.

The Indians could not undertake any widespread cultivation of the plains not only because they lacked iron tools but also because they had no draft animals. The buffalo was too big, too fierce, and too stupid to be domesticated. In all the length and breadth of the two Americas there was no animal to take the place of the useful horse, donkey, or ox. The llama was too small to do anything but carry light loads, and it could live only in a most limited area among the cold Andean highlands. Even if the aboriginal Americans could have made iron ploughs, they could not have ploughed the tough sod without the aid of animals. Moreover, even if the possession of metal tools and beasts of burden had made agriculture possible in the grass-lands, it would have been difficult, in the absence of wood for fences, to prevent the buffalo from eating up the crops or at least from tramping through them and spoiling them. Thus the fertile land of the great plains remained largely unused until the white man came to the New World bringing the iron tools and domestic animals that were necessary to successful agriculture.

Although farming of any sort was almost as impossible in the plains as in the dry regions of winter rains farther west, the abundance of buffaloes made life much easier in many respects. It is astonishing to see how many purposes these animals served. An early traveler who dwelt among one of the buffalo-hunting tribes, the Tonkawa of central Texas, says: "Besides their meat it [the buffalo] furnishes them liberally what they desire for conveniences. The brains are used to soften skins, the horns for spoons and drinking cups, the shoulder blades to dig up and clear off the ground, the tendons for threads and bow strings, the hoofs to glue the arrow-feathering. From the tail-hair they make ropes and girths, from the wool, belts and various ornaments. The hide furnishes . . . shields, tents, shirts, footwear, and blankets to protect them from the cold."[1]

The buffalo is a surprisingly stupid animal. When a herd is feeding it is possible for a man to walk into the midst of it and shoot down an animal. Even when one of their companions falls dead, the buffaloes pay no attention to the hunter provided he remains perfectly still. The wounded animals are not at first dangerous but seek to flee. Only when pursued and brought to bay do they turn on their pursuers. When the Indians of an encampment united their forces, as was their regular habit, they were able to slaughter hundreds of animals in a few days. The more delicate parts of the meat they ate first, often without cooking them. The rest they dried and packed away for future use, while they prepared the hides as coverings for the tents or as rugs in which to sleep.

Wherever the buffaloes were present in large numbers, the habits of the Indians were much the same. They could not live in settled villages, for there was no assurance that the buffalo would come to any particular place each year. The plains tribes were therefore more thoroughly nomadic than al-

[1] See Hodge, *Handbook of American Indians*, vol. II, p. 781.

most any others, especially after the introduction
of horses. Because they wandered so much, they
came into contact with other tribes to an unusual
degree, and much of the contact was friendly.
Gradually the Indians developed a sign language
by which tribes of different tongues could com-
municate with one another. At first these signs
were like pictographs, for the speaker pointed as
nearly as possible to the thing that he desired to indicate, but later they became more and more con-
ventional. For example, man, the erect animal, was
indicated by throwing up the hand, with its back
outward and the index finger extending upward.
Woman was indicated by a sweeping downward
movement of the hand at the side of the head with
fingers extended to denote long hair or the combing
of flowing locks.

Among the plains Indians, the Dakotas, the
main tribe of the Sioux family, are universally
considered to have stood highest not only physically but mentally, and probably morally. Their
bravery was never questioned, and they con-
quered or drove out every rival except the Chip-
pewas. Their superiority was clearly seen in their
system of government. Personal fitness and pop-
ularity determined chieftainship more than did

heredity. The authority of the chief was limited by the Band Council, without whose approbation little or nothing could be accomplished. In one of the Dakota tribes, the Tetons, the policing of a village was confided to two or three officers who were appointed by the chief and who remained in power until their successors were appointed. Day and night they were always on the watch, and so arduous were their labors that their term of service was necessarily short. The brevity of their term, however, was atoned for by the greatness of their authority, for in the suppression of disturbances no resistance was suffered. Their persons were sacred, and if in the execution of their duty they struck even a chief of the second class they could not be punished.

The Dakotas, who lived in the region where their name is still preserved, inhabited that part of the great plain which is climatically most favorable to great activity. It is perhaps because of their response to the influence of this factor of geographical environment that they and their neighbors are the best known of the plains tribes. Their activity in later times is evident from the fact that the Tetons were called "the plundering Arabs of America." If their activities had been more wisely directed, they might have made a great name for themselves in Indian history. In the arts they stood as high as could be expected in view of the wandering life which they led and the limited materials with which they had to work. In the art of making pictographs, for instance, they excelled all other tribes, except perhaps the Kiowas, a plains tribe of Colorado and western Kansas. On the hides of buffalo, deer, and antelope which formed their tents, the Dakotas painted calendars, which had a picture for each year, or rather for each winter, while those of the Kiowas had a summer symbol and a winter symbol. Probably these calendars reveal the influence of the whites, but they at least show that these people of the plains were quick-witted.

Farther south the tribes of the plains stood on a much lower level than the Dakotas. The Spanish explorer, Cabeza de Vaca, describes the Yguases in Texas, among whom he lived for several years, in these words: "Their support is principally roots which require roasting two days. Many are very bitter. Occasionally they take deer and at times fish, but the quantity is so small and the famine so great that they eat spiders and eggs of ants, worms, lizards, salamanders, snakes, and vipers that kill whom they strike, and they eat earth and all that there is, the dung of deer, things I omit to mention and I earnestly believe that were there stones in that land they would eat them. They save the bones of the fish they consume, the snakes and other animals, that they may afterward beat them together and eat the powder." During these painful periods, they bade Cabeza de Vaca "not to be sad. There would soon be prickly pears, although the season of this fruit of the cactus might be months distant. When the pears were ripe, the people feasted and danced and forgot their former privations. They destroyed their female infants to prevent them being taken by their enemies and thus becoming the means of increasing the latter's number."

East of the Great Plains there dwelt still another important type of Indians, the people of the deciduous forests. Their home extended from the Great Lakes to the Gulf of Mexico. As we have already seen, the Iroquois who inhabited the northern part of this region were in many respects the highest product of aboriginal America. The northern Iroquois tribes, especially those known as the Five Nations, were second to no other Indian people north of Mexico in political organization, state-

craft, and military prowess. Their leaders were
genuine diplomats, as the wily French and English
statesmen with whom they treated soon discovered. One of their most notable traits was the
reverence which they had for the tribal law. The
wars that they waged were primarily for political
independence, for the fundamental principle of
their confederation was that by uniting with one
another they would secure the peace and welfare
of all with whom they were connected by ties of
blood. They prevented blood feuds by decreeing
that there should be a price for the killing of a co-
tribesman, and they abstained from eating the
flesh of their enemies in order to avoid future strife.
So thoroughly did they believe in the rights of the
individual that women were accorded a high position. Among some of the tribes the consent of all
the women who had borne children was required
before any important measure could be taken.
Candidates for a chiefship were nominated by the
votes of the mothers, and, as lands and houses
were the property of the women, their power in
the tribe was great.

The Iroquois were sedentary and agricultural,
and depended on the chase for only a small part
of their existence. The northern tribes were

especially noted for their skill in building fortifications and houses. Their so-called castles were solid wooden structures with platforms running around the top on the inside. From the platforms stones and other missiles could be hurled down upon besiegers. According to our standards such dwellings were very primitive, but they were almost as great an advance upon the brush piles of the Utes as our skyscrapers are upon them.

Farther south in the Carolinas, the Cherokees, another Iroquoian tribe, stand out prominently by reason of their unusual mental ability. Under the influence of the white man, the Cherokees were the first to adopt a constitutional form of government embodied in a code of laws written in their own language. Their language was reduced to writing by means of an alphabet which one of their number named Sequoya had devised. Sequoya and other leaders, however, may not have been pure Indians, for by that time much white blood had been mixed with the tribe. Yet even before the coming of the white man the Cherokees were apparently more advanced in agriculture than the Iroquois were, but less advanced in their form of government, in their treatment of women, and in many other respects.

In general, as we go from north to south in the region of deciduous forests, we find that among the early Indians agriculture became more and more important and the people more sedentary, though not always more progressive in other ways. The Catawbas, for instance, in South Carolina were sedentary agriculturists and seem to have differed little in general customs from their neighbors. Their men were brave and honest but lacking in energy. In the Muskhogean family of Indians, comprising the Creeks, Choctaws, Chickasaws, and Seminoles, who occupied the Gulf States from Georgia to Mississippi, all the tribes were agricultural and sedentary and occupied villages of substantial houses. The towns near the tribal frontiers were usually palisaded, but those more remote from invasion were unprotected. All these Indians were brave but not warlike in the violent fashion of the Five Nations. The Choctaws would fight only in self-defense, it was said, but the Creeks and especially the Chickasaws were more aggressive. In their government these Muskhogean tribes appear to have attained a position corresponding to their somewhat advanced culture in other respects. Yet their confederacies were loose and flimsy compared with that of the Five Nations.

Another phase of the life of the tribes in the southern part of the region of deciduous forests is illustrated by the Natchez of Mississippi. These people were strictly sedentary and depended chiefly upon agriculture for a livelihood. They possessed considerable skill in the arts. For instance, they wove a cloth from the inner bark of the mulberry tree and made excellent pottery. They also constructed great mounds of earth upon which to erect their dwellings and temples. Like a good many of the other southern tribes, they fought when it was necessary, but they were peaceable compared with the Five Nations. They had a form of sun-worship resembling that of Mexico, and in other ways their ideas were like those of the people farther south. For instance, when a chief died, his wives were killed. In times of distress the parents frequently offered their children as sacrifice.

Many characteristics of the Natchez and other southern tribes seem to indicate that they had formerly possessed a civilization higher than that which prevailed when the white man came. The Five Nations, on the contrary, apparently represent an energetic people who were on the upward path and who might have achieved great things if

the whites had not interrupted them. The southern Indians resemble people whose best days were
past, for the mounds which abound in the Gulf
States appear to have been built chiefly in pre-
Columbian days. Their objects of art, such as
the remarkable wooden mortars found at Key
Marco and the embossed copper plates found elsewhere in Florida, point to a highly developed
artistic sense which was no longer in evidence at
the coming of the white man.

It is interesting to see the way in which climatic
energy tended to give the Five Nations a marked
superiority over the tribesmen of the South, while
agriculture tended in the opposite direction.
There has been much discussion as to the part
played by agriculture among the primitive Americans, especially in the northeast. Corn, beans, and
squashes were an important element in the diet
of the Indians of the New England region, while
farther south potatoes, sunflower seeds, and melons
were also articles of food. The New England
tribes knew enough about agriculture to use fish
and shells for fertilizer. They had wooden mat-
tocks and hoes made from the shoulder blades of
deer, from tortoise shells, or from conch shells set
in handles. They also had stone hoes and spades,

while the women used short pickers or parers about a foot long and five inches wide. Seated on the ground they used these to break the upper part of the soil and to grub out weeds, grass, and old corn-stalks. They had the regular custom of burning over an old patch each year and then replanting it. Sometimes they merely put the seeds in holes and sometimes they dug up and loosened the ground for each seed. Clearings they made by girdling the trees, that is, by cutting off the bark in a circle at the bottom and thus causing the tree to die. The brush they hacked or broke down and burned when it was dry enough.

There is much danger of confusing the agricul-tural condition of the Indian after the European had modified his life with his condition before the European came to America. For instance, in the excellent article on agriculture in the *Handbook of American Indians*, conditions prevailing as late as 1794 in the States south of the Great Lakes are spoken of as if typical of aboriginal America. But at that time the white man had long been in con-tact with the Indian, and iron tools had largely taken the place of stone. The rapidity with which European importations spread may be judged by the fact that as early as 1736 the Iroquois in

New York not only had obtained horses but were regularly breeding them. The use of the iron axe of course spread with vastly greater rapidity than that of the horse, for an axe or a knife was the first thing that an Indian sought from the white man. In the eighteenth century agriculture had thus become immeasurably easier than before, yet even then the Indians still kept up their old habit of cultivating the same fields only a short time. The regular practice was to cultivate a field five, ten, and sometimes even twenty or more years, and then abandon it.[1]

What hindered agriculture most in the northern part of the deciduous forest was the grass. Any one who has cultivated a garden knows how rapidly the weeds grow. He also knows that there is no weed so hard to exterminate as grass. When once it gets a foothold mere hoeing seems only to make

[1] Ordinarily it is stated that this practice was due to the exhaustion of the soil. That, however, is open to question, for five or ten years' desultory cultivation on the part of the Indian would scarcely exhaust the soil so much that people would go to the great labor of making new clearings and moving their villages. Moreover, in the Southern States it is well known today that the soil is exhausted much more rapidly than farther north because it contains less humus. Nevertheless the southern tribes cultivated the land about their villages for long periods. Tribes like the Creeks, the Cherokees, and the Natchez appear to have been decidedly less prone to move than the Iroquois, in spite of the relatively high development of these northern nations.

it grow the faster. The only way to get rid of grass when once it has become well established is to plow the field and start over again, but this the Indians could not do. When first a clearing was made in the midst of the forest, there was no grass to be contended with. Little by little, however, it was sure to come in, until at length what had been a garden was in a fair way to become a meadow. Then the Indians would decide that it was necessary to seek new fields.

One might suppose that under such circumstances the Indians would merely clear another patch of forest not far from the village and so continue to live in the old place. This, however, they did not do because the labor of making a clearing with stone axes and by the slow process of girdling and burning the trees was so great that it was possible only in certain favored spots where by accident the growth was less dense than usual. When once a clearing became grassy, the only thing to do was to hunt for a new site, prepare a clearing, and then move the village. This was apparently the reason why the Iroquois, although successful in other ways, failed to establish permanent towns like those of the Pueblos and the Haidas. Their advancement not only in architecture but in many of the most important elements of civilization was for this reason greatly delayed. There was little to stimulate them to improve the land to which they were attached, for they knew that soon they would have to move.

Farther south the character of the grassy vegetation changes, and the condition of agriculture alters with it. The grass ceases to have that thick, close, turfy quality which we admire so much in the fields of the north, and it begins to grow in bunches. Often a southern hillside may appear from a distance to be as densely covered with grass as a New England hayfield. On closer examination, however, the growth is seen to consist of individual bunches which can easily be pulled up, so that among the southern tribes the fields did not become filled with grass as they did in the north, for the women had relatively little difficulty in keeping out this kind of weed as well as others.

In this survey of aboriginal America we have been impressed by the contrast between two diverse aspects of the control of human activities by physical environment. We saw, in the first place, that in our own day the distribution of culture in America is more closely related to climatic energy than to any other factor, because man is now so advanced in the arts and crafts that agricultural difficulties do not impede him, except in the far north and in tropical forests.

Secondly, we have found that, although all the geographical factors acted upon the Indian as they do today, the absence of metals and beasts of burden compelled man to be nomadic, and hence to remain in a low stage of civilization in many places where he now can thrive.

In the days long before Columbus the distribution of civilization in the Red Man's Continent offered still a third aspect, strikingly different both from that of today and from that of the age of discovery. In that earlier period the great centers of civilization were south of their present situation. In the southern part of North America from Arizona to Florida there are abundant evidences that the Indians whom the white man found were less advanced than their predecessors. The abundant ruins of Arizona and New Mexico, their widespread distribution, and the highly artistic character of the pottery and other products of handicraft found in them seem to indicate that the ancient population was both denser and more highly cultured than that which the Europeans finally ousted. In the

THE GOVERNOR'S PALACE AT UXMAL, YUCATAN, MEXICO

Wood engraving in Ancient Cities of the New World, by Désiré Charnay.

Bravure Anderson—Lamb Co.N.Y.

Gulf States there is perhaps not much evidence that there was a denser population at an earlier period, but the excellence of the pre-Columbian handicrafts and the existence of a decadent sun worship illustrate the way in which the civilization of the past was higher than that of later days.

The Aztecs, who figure so largely in the history of the exploration and conquest of Mexico, were merely a warlike tribe which had been fortunate in the inheritance of a relatively high civilization from the past. So, too, the civilization found by the Spaniards at places such as Mitla, in the extreme south of Mexico, could not compare with that of which evidence is found in the ruins. Most remarkable of all is the condition of Yucatan and Guatemala. In northern Yucatan the Spaniards found a race of mild, decadent Mayas living among the relics of former grandeur. Although they used the old temples as shrines, they knew little of those who had built these temples and showed still less capacity to imitate the ancient architects. Farther south in the forested region of southern Yucatan and northern Guatemala the conditions are still more surprising, for today these regions are almost uninhabitable and are occupied by only a few sickly, degraded natives who live largely by the chase. Yet in the past this region was the scene of by far the highest culture that ever developed in America. There alone in this great continent did men develop an architecture which, not only in massiveness but in wealth of architectural detail and sculptural adornment, vies with that of early Egypt or Chaldea. There alone did the art of writing develop. Yet today in those regions the density of the forest, the prevalence of deadly fevers, the extremely enervating temperature, and the steady humidity are as hostile to civilization as are the cold of the far north and the dryness of the desert.

The only explanation of this anomaly seems to be that in the past the climatic zones of the world have at certain periods been shifted farther toward the equator than they are at present. Practically all the geographers of America now believe that within the past two or three thousand years climatic pulsations have taken place whereby places like the dry Southwest have alternately experienced centuries of greater moisture than at present and centuries as dry as today or even drier. During the moist centuries greater storminess prevailed, so that the climate was apparently better not only for agriculture but for human energy. At such times the standard of living was higher than now not only in the Southwest but in the Gulf States and in Mexico. In periods when the deserts of the southwestern United States were wet, the Maya region of Yucatan and Guatemala appears to have been relatively dry. Then the dry belt which now extends from northern Mexico to the northern tip of Yucatan apparently shifted southward. Such conditions would cause the forests of Yucatan and Guatemala to become much less dense than at present. This comparative deforestation would make agriculture easily possible where today it is out of the question. At the same time the relatively dry climate and the clearing away of the vegetation would to a large degree eliminate the malarial fevers and other diseases which are now such a terrible scourge in wet tropical countries. Then, too, the storms which at the present time give such variability to the climate of the United States would follow more southerly courses. In its stimulating qualities the climate of the home of the Mayas in the days of their prime was much more nearly like that which now prevails where civilization rises highest.

From first to last the civilization of America has been bound up with its physical environment. It matters little whether we are dealing with the red race, the black, or the white. Nor does it matter whether we deal with one part of the continent or another. Wherever we turn we can trace the influence of mountains and plains, of rocks and metals from which tools are made, of water and its finny inhabitants, of the beasts of the chase from the hare to the buffalo, of domestic animals, of the native forests, grass-lands, and deserts, and, last but not least, of temperature, moisture, and wind in their direct effects upon the human body. At one stage of human development the possibilities of agriculture may be the dominant factor in man's life in early America. At another, domestic animals may be more important, and at still another, iron or waterways or some other factor may be predominant. It is the part of the later history of the American Continent to trace the effect of these various factors and to chronicle the influence that they have had upon man's progress.

BIBLIOGRAPHICAL NOTE

ALTHOUGH many books deal with the physical features of the Western Hemisphere and many others with the Indians, few deal with the two in relation to one another. One book, however, stands out preëminent in this respect, namely, Edward John Payne's *History of the New World Called America*, 2 vols. (1892–99). This book, which has never been finished, attempts to explain the conditions of life among the American aborigines as the result of geographical conditions, especially of the food supply. Where the author carries this attempt into the field of special customs and religious rites, he goes too far. Nevertheless his work is uncommonly stimulating and deserves the careful attention of the reader who would gain a broad grasp of the relation of geography to the history of the New World.

Two other good books which deal with the relation of geography to American history are Miss Ellen C. Semple's *American History and its Geographical Conditions* (1903) and A. P. Brigham's *Geographic Influences in American History* (1903). Both of these books interpret geography as if it included little except the form of the land. While they bring out clearly the effect of mountain barriers. indented coasts, and easy routes whether by land or water, they scarcely touch on the more subtle relationships between man on the one hand

and the climate, plants, and animals which form the
dominant features of his physical environment on the
other hand.

In their emphasis on the form of the land both Semple
and Brigham follow the lead of W. M. Davis. In his
admirable articles on America and the United States in
The Encyclopædia Britannica (11th edition) and in *The
International Geography* edited by H. R. Mill (1901),
Davis has given an uncommonly clear and vivid descrip-
tion of the main physical features of the New World.
Living beings, however, play little part in this descrip-
tion, so that the reader is not led to an understanding
of how physical geography affects human actions.

Other good descriptions of the North American continent are found in the following books: I. C. Russell's
North America (1904), Stanford's *Compendium of Modern
Geography and Travel*, including the volumes on Canada,
the United States, and Central America, and the great
volumes on America in *The Earth and its Inhabitants* by
Élisée Reclus, 19 vols. (1876–1894). Russell's book is
largely physiographic but contains some good chapters
on the Indians. In Stanford's *Compendium* the purpose is to treat man and nature in their relation to one
another, but the relationships are not clearly brought
out, and there is too much emphasis on purely de-
scriptive and encyclopedic matter. So far as interest is
concerned, the famous work by Élisée Reclus holds high
rank. It is an encyclopedia of geographical facts arranged and edited in such a way that it has all the interest of a fine book of travel. Like most of the other
books, however, it fails to bring out relationships.

As sources of information on the Indians, two books
stand out with special prominence. *The American Race,*

by D. G. Brinton (1891), is a most scholarly volume devoted largely to a study of the Indians on a linguistic
basis. It contains some general chapters, however, on
the Indians and their environment, and these are most
illuminating.   The other book is the *Handbook of American Indians North of Mexico*, edited by F. W. Hodge,
and published by the United States Bureau of Ethnology (Washington, 1897, 1910, 1911).   Its two large
volumes are arranged in encyclopedic form.   The various articles are written by a large number of scholars,
including practically all the students who were at work
on Indian ethnology at the time of publication.   Many
of the articles are the best that have been written and
will not only interest the general reader but will contribute to an understanding of what America was when
the Indians came here and what it still is today.

INDEX

Adirondack Mountains, 64

Africa, migration from, 4; position on earth, 37; backwardness of indigenous life in, 39

Agriculture, cotton production, 70; in tropical forests, 104–106; advantages of desert for, 116–17; influence on civilization, 124–25; in California, 140–42; of Hopi Indians, 147–148, 149–50; difficulties on the plains, 151–52; Catawba, 161; Muskhogean, 161; Iroquois, 163–67

Alabama, "cotton belt" in, 70

Alaska, probable migrations by way of, 15–21; climate, 18; effect of climate on white men, 18–20; probable effect on Indians, 20–21

Aleutian Islands supposed route of red men, 15–16, 17–18

Alleghany plateau, 64–66

Altoona, escarpment at, 64, 67

Amazon River, 22, 49

America, migrations to, 2–4; inverse resemblances to Old World, 40 *et seq.*; *see also* Cordillera, North America, South America

Andes Mountains, 41–42

Animal life, of Asia, 12–13; in northern forests, 92, 128; musk-ox, 106–07; no draft animals, 152; buffalo, 153–154

Annapolis, tests of mentality at, 10

Antarctica, 37, 42

Appalachian highland, 3; one of physical divisions of North America, 51; character and extent, 59–60; eastern crystalline band, 60–62; second band, valley, 62–64; third band, Alleghany plateau, 64–66; routes over, 67

Archæan V, 51

Archeology, indications of preglacial man, 11–12; ruins of Arizona and New Mexico, 168

Arctic Ocean, position on earth, 37; drainage into, 42

Arizona, plateaus of, 76; Painted Desert, 97; desert, 113–14; climate, 148–50; ruins in, 168

Asia, migrations from, 4, 12–14; man's original home, 11–12; climatic variation in, 13; position on earth, 37; cordillera in, 41

Athabasca, Lake, 54

Athapascan Indians, 118, 127–129

Atlantic coast, resemblances between that of America and Old World, 45–47

Atlantic coastal plain, 68–70

Atlantic Ocean, position on earth, 37; drainage into, 42

Australia, position on earth, 37; backwardness of indigenous life in, 39–40

Aztecs, 119, 169

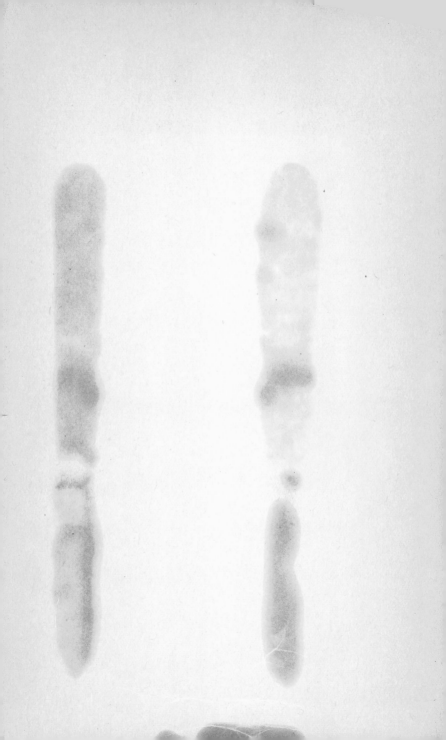